Breathe
Easy

Breathe
Easy

*De-stress, build confidence
and focus your mind
in seven days*

Dr David Lewis

Vermilion
LONDON

Dedication: To Ricky and Liz in grateful appreciation of all their help and encouragement in the writing of this book.

1 3 5 7 9 10 8 6 4 2

First published 2002 by Vermilion,
an imprint of Ebury Press · Random House
20 Vauxhall Bridge Road · London SW1V 2SA
www.randomhouse.co.uk

Random House Australia (Pty) Limited
20 Alfred Street · Milsons Point · Sydney
New South Wales 2061 · Australia

Random House New Zealand Limited
18 Poland Road · Glenfield · Auckland 10 · New Zealand

Random House South Africa (Pty) Limited
Endulini · 5a Jubilee Road · Parktown 2193 · South Africa

The Random House Group Limited Reg. No. 954009

Papers used by Vermilion are natural, recyclable products made
from wood grown in sustainable forests.

Printed and bound in Great Britain by Mackays of Chatham plc, Chatham, Kent

Designed by Lovelock & Co.
Illustrations by Stuart Johnson

A CIP catalogue record for this book is available from
the British Library.

ISBN 009188225 7

Contents

Acknowledgements

I would like to thank the many sportsmen and women who have contributed to my understanding of the achievement of peak mental and physical performance under intense competitive pressure. These included: Colin Montgomery; Nick Faldo and David Leadbetter (golf); Jeremy Bates and Jo Dury (tennis); Jonathan Edwards (long jump); Steven Backley (javelin); Jacques Villeneuve and Frank Williams (Formula I racing) ; Jonah Lomu and Phil Kingsly Jones (rugby); Mark Foster and David Haller (swimming); Liz McColgan and Grete Waitz (marathon running); Chris Boardman and Peter Keen (cycling); Steve Smith and Mike Holmes (high jump); Colin McRae and Derek Rager (rally driving); Tani Grey (Para Olympics gold medallist); Colin Jackson and Malcolm Arnold (110 m hurdles); Jurgen Grobler, Colin Redgrave and Mathew Pinsent (rowing); Jane Torville and Christopher Dean (ice-skating); John Regis and Mike McFarlane (sprint); Mick Doohan and Jerry Burgess (speedway); Jenny and Mark Pitman (horse racing).

I should also like to thank Lee Ashworth, sports physiologist and triathlete, for his assistance in the research and training programmes from which the procedures you will learn in this book were developed.

Last, but certainly not least, my grateful thanks to Keelan Leyser and Steven Matthews for reading a draft of the manuscript and for his invaluable comments and suggestions.

Introduction

'Everyone has a will to win, but very few have a will to prepare.'
VINCE LOMBARDI – THE US FOOTBALL COACH AFTER
WHOM THE SUPERBOWL TROPHY IS NAMED.

This is a practical book designed to serve a practical purpose. It has been written to assist you in achieving your goals by ensuring that, whatever the challenge, you will be able to function at the peak of your mental and physical potential.

Over recent years, sports psychology – pioneered with great success in the USA and former Soviet Union – is increasingly becoming recognized as a vital component of every serious athlete's training programme. More recently many of the procedures that have enabled athletes constantly to improve their personal best performances have been introduced into the workplace. This book explains why such procedures work, how to carry them out and what they can do to help you achieve your own personal best in any activity you attempt. Its goal is to help you become the person you want and deserve to be.

For more than twenty years I have been fascinated by similarities between the demands of sporting success and achievement in the world of work. Each demands intense focus and self-discipline, as well as courage, confidence and persistence in the face of frustrations and setbacks. In my research I have worked with élite athletes as well as executives and employees at all levels from major multinational companies. In the laboratory I have used specialist bio-monitoring equipment to study exactly what is going on in brain and body when people are confronted by a personal or professional challenge. I have also been consulted by a wide range of private clients eager to achieve their true potential in life and unable to understand exactly what is preventing them from doing so. You can read some of their stories in Chapters One and Two. (Incidentally, as is customary when using case histories, all the names of my clients, as well as some minor personal details, have been changed in order to protect their confidentiality and anonymity.) In training workshops around the world I have helped participants achieve their personal best in activities ranging from managing multinational companies to their speed in athletics championships.

Some fifteen years ago I published the initial findings of my research in a book entitled *The Alpha Plan*, which formed the basis of many of my subsequent training programmes. It was also the subject of a BBC TV documentary in which four of my clients – including the programme's presenter – underwent training to overcome a variety of seemingly minor, but to them intensely frustrating, barriers to their future development. All did well and their eventual triumphs, which ranged from overcoming social anxiety to improving times in a cycle race, were duly recorded on film.

Since then I have continued with my research and training programmes, both in the UK and continental Europe, aimed at exploring and harnessing the power of the human breath to influence performance via its effects on electrical activity in the brain. The results, tailored to a home-based, easily followed training programme, are presented for the first time in *Breathe Easy*. It will show you how to ensure that every important activity you undertake in life, from playing a sport, attending a job interview or closing a multi-million dollar deal, is performed at the peak of your mental and physical potential. The training is based on three key findings:

1. A failure to realize our true potential is often due to barriers arising below our level of normal conscious awareness in a more ancient region of the brain known as the limbic system. This area of the brain, and the powerful influence it exerts over our thoughts and behaviour, will be fully described in Chapter Five.

2. These barriers cannot usually be removed by means of encouraging words, rational arguments or logical reasoning. This is because the limbic system cannot understand or respond to verbal instructions from the higher regions of the brain. Its language consists not of words but of vivid images, sounds, aromas and other physical sensations.

3. As these barriers originated in subtle changes to our rate or depth of breathing they can only be eliminated by learning new ways of breathing – patterns of breathwork that create a state of mind in which the limbic system is maximally receptive to new commands.

It is through the breath that these emotional barriers to achievement first arose and through the breath that they may be eliminated. For this reason I have termed the method by which this process occurs **BO-TAU** or **B**reath **O**ptimized **T**ransactional **U**nlocking.

In the training programme that comprises Part Two of this book you will find six procedures for improving all aspects of performance, from reducing stress and enhancing concentration to removing emotional barriers to success. By selecting the one best suited to your current needs and practising for a few minutes each day you will be able to eliminate subconscious barriers to progress and achieve all that lies within your power to accomplish.

David Lewis,
Les Genet,
Var, France

Part One

NEW MIND – NEW BODY

If the human mind new half as much as the human brain
we would be twice as smart and ten times more successful.

CHAPTER ONE

How to be all you want to be

'To be what we are, and to become what we are capable of becoming, is the only end of life.'
ROBERT LOUIS STEVENSON (1850–1894)

I am sitting in my consulting room with a client named Jason and watching three coloured lines moving across the computer screen before me.

The first line is blue and traces a rhythmic pattern of hills and valleys representing the slow, deep rise and fall of his breathing. This information is being transmitted to the computer via two transducers that measure changes in the tension of broad elastic straps passing around Jason's chest and fastened behind his back.

The second line on my monitor is red and shows variations in the level of Jason's physiological arousal. Two small electrodes, each approximately a centimetre in diameter, are attached to his left palm and measure electrical resistance within his body. As he relaxes more and more deeply this resistance significantly increases. Conversely the more anxious or agitated he becomes the less resistance there is to the electric current. While the red line on my monitor continues to rise, I know that Jason's relaxation is deepening. If, however, it should start to drop steeply that would alert me to the fact he is becoming far more physically tense. The faster the line drops the more rapidly his anxiety would be increasing.

The third line on the screen, a green one, indicates electrical activity within Jason's brain. This EEG signal (Electroencephalogram) is being monitored by a series of electrodes attached to his skull through parted hair. These are measuring just a few millionths of a volt across a range of frequencies from very slow, so-called, Delta waves, to much faster Beta waves ranging from fewer than 4 cycles per second up to 35 or more.

I shall have much more to say about these brain waves in Chapter Eight but for the moment just note that brain waves with a frequency of between 8 and 14 cycles per second, called Alpha waves, dominate the EEG of people whose mental state is one of relaxed alertness.

At the moment we have joined Jason's therapy session, he is lying back in a comfortable chair with his eyes closed and, guided by my words, developing a vivid sensualization in his mind's eye. 'Sensualizing' is the name I give to a very special procedure for developing what amounts to a virtual reality world behind the eyes. Unlike a visualization, in which you merely seek to picture events, this procedure incorporates information from all five senses.

In his virtual-reality world Jason is walking across the golden sands of a beautiful tropical island he has learned to make his own private and personal paradise. It is a serene place where he feels secure and relaxed. Although it exists only in his own mind this island has become, during six treatment sessions, as vividly real as any other place he has visited on earth.

With his eyes closed Jason clearly *sees* himself on the sun-drenched beach and *hears* the surf gently breaking on the fine, golden sands. He *feels* the beach warm beneath his bare feet and the sun at his back. He *smells* the sweetly scented tropical flowers along the edge of the palm-fringed foreshore. When he swims in the crystal clear waters he *senses* its coolness around his body, as well as the movements his muscles make while propelling him through the shimmering ocean.

As Jason lies back and becomes more and more completely absorbed by this sensualization all my instruments show him to be very deeply relaxed. The blue line tells me that his rate of breathing has come down from around eighteen breaths per minute to fewer than four breaths per minute. And from being light and shallow when he had entered the consulting room some ten minutes earlier, his breathing is now heavy and deep, with each inhalation drawing the air down into the lower lobes of his lungs and every exhalation expelling almost all the stale air. The red line is showing a state of almost complete physical relaxation. There is little or no unnecessary stress or tension in any of his more than 600 muscles. The green line of his EEG shows a brain in which the slowly moving Alpha waves predominate.

Like many busy, successful and ambitious men and women, such deep mental and physical relaxation is not something with which Jason has been very familiar. In his high-pressure career as marketing director for a rapidly expanding IT company, every day passes in a frenetic rush to keep deadlines, attend meetings and deliver on time. His working life includes almost constant travel combined with long hours behind a computer in order to keep ahead of the game in a relentlessly competitive global industry.

At thirty-nine Jason is an extremely fit man. Always a sports enthusiast he ran for his university and still works out three times a week in a gym, swims fifty lengths of his local swimming pool most weekends and rides a mountain bike whenever he gets the chance — which is why the sudden onset of panic attacks so profoundly unnerved him.

The first time it happened, immediately before he rose to present some crucial proposals to a group of investors, Jason believed himself to be having a heart attack. He could feel his heart pounding relentlessly and unevenly in his chest. He broke out into such a sweat that the fluid poured from his face and soaked his shirt. He felt giddy and believed he was on the point of fainting. His breathing became so tight and painful that he thought he was about to suffocate. Pale and trembling he stumbled from the conference room and just made it to the lavatory before passing out. The next thing he remembers is the blaring of an ambulance siren as he was rushed into a hospital emergency room. But by the time he got there he felt perfectly all right again and the cardiologist could find nothing wrong with his heart. Deeply embarrassed and feeling a complete fraud, Jason returned to his office and put it down to food poisoning.

When the same thing happened on two further occasions, both times immediately before he was due to make an important presentation, Jason checked himself into a private clinic for a series of tests. After the doctors had finished their investigations and reviewed the results they told him he there was nothing physically the matter. He was suffering from intense anxiety leading to panic attacks at the prospect of having to speak in public, a condition known as lallophobia.

At first Jason flatly refused to accept the diagnosis. It seemed inconceivable to him that anyone so physically and – as he believed himself to be – mentally stable could fall victim to anything which seemed tainted by what he regarded as the stigma of mental illness. It took two more attacks, the last one occurring as he was actually rising to deliver a rousing message to 500 employees at his company's annual conference, before Jason was prepared to accept that his difficulties had a psychological rather than a physical basis. This brings us back to his seventh session in my consulting rooms and the reason why he was wired up to my bio-monitoring equipment.

For the past six sessions I had concentrated on assisting Jason to relax deeply. Today I intended to move the treatment one step further forward and begin exploring exactly what was going on when he prepared to speak in public. For this I began to guide him through a different sensualization. Now, instead of the tranquil tropical island, I asked him to imagine he was about to make a brief presentation on a very familiar topic to a small group of friendly colleagues. I started in this very modest and, hopefully, only mildly threatening way in order to identify at what point he would start to become fearful. Almost as soon as he started sensualizing the scene, however, my instruments told me that Jason was growing anxious.

On my computer screen I observed three things happening almost, but not quite, simultaneously. First, and the sequence of events is important, his rate of breathing slightly and subtly altered. The smoothly flowing hills and valleys of each inhalation and exhalation suddenly became steeper and closer until they resembled a zigzag range of jagged mountain peaks. This clearly told me that his breathing was becoming faster, shallower and more erratic. Almost immediately after his breathing altered, the thin red line monitoring Jason's physiological arousal dived towards the bottom of the screen showing rapidly increasing anxiety. Finally, the output of Alpha waves yielded ground to faster Beta frequencies, indicating growing mental agitation. All this happened less than three seconds after he 'sensualized' public speaking.

Yet when I asked Jason how he was feeling, he replied that he was reasonably calm and perfectly capable of handling the impending challenge. Clearly his unconscious mind knew something of which his conscious brain was unaware. Not until almost 30 seconds had passed, during which his breathing became even more rapid, erratic and shallow while his physical and mental arousal soared, did Jason report the sensation of a rising tide of panic. He abruptly opened his eyes and blurted: 'It's no good. I'm sorry. I simply can't deal with this. I can feel my heart racing, my mouth has gone dry and all I could think of was to escape from the situation.'

I'll be returning to Jason and the reasons why he developed a public-speaking phobia in Chapter Two. For the moment let's just recap on the sequence of events within his mind and body immediately prior to his overwhelming sensation of total panic.

First the pattern of his breathing changed, only slightly at first but still enough to trigger subtle changes in the chemical composition of his blood. By removing more carbon dioxide from his bloodstream the rapid breathing stimulated his nervous system, so increasing physical arousal. This occurred as the 'fight or flight' response – a primitive and powerful survival mechanism – triggering a region of his brain called the limbic system. I shall be describing the crucial role of this primitive region of the brain in influencing performance in Chapter Five. Finally his brain waves altered from the relaxed but alert Alpha state to one dominated by the fast moving Beta frequencies associated with mental agitation. Note, however, that all this happened below his level of conscious awareness. Even after body and brain had switched into a 'prepare to panic' mode, the conscious part of Jason's mind remained reasonably cool, calm and confident. It was as if a householder were watching TV, blissfully ignorant of a fire gathering strength in his basement and about to burst through the floorboards beneath his feet!

The point I want to emphasise here is that Jason's *breathing* was the first thing to change and that it was this change that triggered the chain reaction that led to panic. This is not, of course, the way we normally view the sequence of events during any form of powerful emotional upset. Whether starting to get anxious or angry, we regard our conscious awareness of that emotion as a trigger for the other changes – rapidly beating heart, dry mouth, churning stomach, unsteady breathing and so forth – that immediately follow. In other words we usually consider the sequence of events to occur as follows:

1. An awareness of rising emotion. We think 'I'm getting scared' or 'I'm beginning to feel annoyed'.
2. We become aware of increased mental and physical arousal. We notice our heart starting to beat faster, our muscles tightening, our mouth becoming dry and the air pumping in and out of our lungs more rapidly.

3. We stand and fight or turn and flee.

This seems such a common-sense chain of events that we seldom think twice about it. Unfortunately it is entirely and misleadingly wrong.

In the next chapter I shall explain what really happens and why a proper understanding of the sequence is vital for breaking through psychological barriers to personal progress.

By making a more detailed study of the case histories of Jason and another of my clients, named Jacquie, we shall be able to see exactly how barriers – I call them breath locks or b-locks for short – arise, and the damaging effects they can exert on personal and professional development.

CHAPTER TWO

How breath locks are formed

'Negative thoughts lead to a negative performance; the connection is as simple as that!'
SALLY GUNNELL, OLYMPIC GOLD MEDALLIST AND WORLD CHAMPION HURDLER

Let's return to Jason the stressed out IT marketing director, whose panic attacks at the prospect of public speaking I described in the previous chapter. Given that the spark that initially triggered his public-speaking phobia was a build-up of work-related stress, what had originally set the scene for that psychological problem to arise? Jason himself had no insight into why he had suddenly, and for no apparent reason, developed these panic attacks. As far as he was concerned they had struck him out of the blue.

After ten weeks of therapy we seemed to be getting no nearer to discovering what was going on in his subconscious. But the truth came startlingly and unexpectedly to light.

I had just started guiding him through a new sensualization that involved him entering a tunnel leading deep into the side of a mountain. It is one I frequently use when helping clients explore mental processes outside normal conscious awareness. (In Part Two I will show you how to use a similar sensualization in order to break through any barriers currently limiting your own performance.)

We began by going through five minutes of deep diaphragmatic breathing followed by the relaxing breath procedure that I will be describing in Part Two (Procedures Two and Three). At that point in the session all the instruments showed Jason to be in a state of deep mental and physical relaxation. His breathing was calm and deep, his physiological arousal levels low and his EEG showed the smooth, slow Alpha rhythms associated with relaxed alertness.

No sooner had Jason started down the tunnel into the mountainside, however, than I saw an abrupt and unexpected change in all these responses. His breathing became faster and his EEG was suddenly dominated by higher Beta frequencies indicating rising mental agitation. At the same time, the red line on the computer monitor, tracing Jason's bodily tensions, plunged precipitously showing a switch into the highly aroused 'fight or flight' mode. In the safe and comfortable surroundings of my consulting room Jason's brain and body were reacting as if he had suddenly come face to face with a ravenous tiger!

This was completely unanticipated on my part since there was no good reason for that sensualization to make him the least bit alarmed. Before we started I had naturally checked, as I always do, that he did not suffer from even mild claustrophobia, since such fears can easily be provoked by imagining oneself entering even the widest and most spacious of tunnels. Jason had assured me he had no such concerns and so the session began. It took several seconds before Jason became consciously aware of these mental and physiological changes. When he did so, his eyes suddenly opened wide and he sat up in a state of startled bewilderment, as surprised as I had been by the unexpected reaction. We ended the session with neither of us any the wiser about why this innocuous sensualization should have triggered such a rapid and profound increase in anxiety.

During the following days Jason reflected on what had happened and tried to work out why had had become so alarmed. But it was not until almost a week later, the day prior to his next appointment, that he woke up in the middle of the night with a vivid and terrifying memory from his childhood.

The more he reflected on this long forgotten incident the more certain Jason became that it was responsible for the subconscious barrier that was ruining his professional life more than thirty years later. When he came to see me, and recounted the events that had taken place when he was five, I too felt that it might well be what had originally created the barrier in his unconscious mind.

Jason's Story

As a small child Jason had lived with his parents on a farm where his father was the manager. Near to the farmhouse was a barn filled with bales of straw where he often played. By early summer many of the bales had been removed, leaving narrow tunnels into the centre of the barn. The darkness and the dust-filled air proved no deterrent to a small, energetic five-year-old and Jason had soon constructed a secret camp deep inside the building. Because it was so dark inside his hideaway, Jason borrowed a torch from his father's office. One morning, unable to find the torch, he took a candle and matches instead. Inside his camp Jason struck a match and, the next instant, the dust-filled air exploded in flames around him. Within seconds the whole barn was ablaze.

Screaming in terror the child began a desperate crawl to safety through tunnels into which flaming brands of straw were falling. Gasping for air as the acrid white smoke filled his lungs, bare knees raw and bleeding from scrambling over the straw, he could feel the searing heat of the flames at his back. Coughing and sobbing he finally emerged into the open air where his distraught father snatched him to safety.

'I remember lying on the ground, yelling my lungs out as my Dad, his boss and some of the other farm workers looked down at me. Their expressions were almost certainly those of fear and relief, but to my confused and guilty mind they were all staring at me accusingly!'

The barn was totally destroyed and only the prompt arrival of the fire brigade saved the farmhouse itself from destruction. 'I was never punished for what I had done. Indeed nobody mentioned it again. But now that I have finally remembered the incident, I understand why I panic at the thought of speaking in public. I now realize that I see before me not my actual audience but that circle of angry and accusing faces.'

Two things may strike you about Jason's graphic account of that near fatal childhood accident. First, is it conceivable that an event so traumatic and terrifying could have been totally forgotten for more than three decades? Second, how can we be sure that this event – horrifying as it undoubtedly must have been – was the trigger that led to panic attacks, under totally different circumstances, so long after the event?

On the first point, there is good evidence that the more traumatic an incident in early childhood the greater the likelihood of it being forgotten, or to use a psychoanalytical term 'repressed.' Such repression is a natural defence mechanism designed to protect the psyche from further pain. However, unless brought to the surface and defused it can remain undetected for years, like a ticking bomb waiting to detonate with devastating effects as soon as conditions are right. As to whether it caused his panic attacks when trying to present to a potentially hostile audience we can never know for sure. However, for the purposes of successful treatment it was enough that Jason *believed* this was the case.

Jason's Therapy

Having brought that memory to the forefront of Jason's mind we were then able to remove the b-lock it had created – using a procedure you will learn in Part Two (Chapter Sixteen: Procedure six). He then went through further sensualizations while in a relaxed mental and physical state. In these he was encouraged to see himself delivering various presentations, starting with a small friendly audience and a topic with which he was very familiar, to, after several weeks, confrontational presentations before a large and somewhat hostile audience.

This well-established cognitive behavioural approach, known as 'progressive desensitization', can be likened to training for a marathon, by starting with short runs that are just within the athlete's capability and then increasing the distance a little each day as fitness improves. Later Jason was also encouraged to accept invitations to speak in public and asked to keep a diary of his thoughts, feelings and behaviour immediately before, during and after each presentation. The information these notes contained were then built into subsequent sensualization sessions. In addition he practised with the relaxing breath procedure (page 164) and focused on breathing correctly throughout the talk.

Within three months Jason's public-speaking phobia almost totally disappeared. While he remained slightly apprehensive prior to a presentation this was a normal and easily managed level of arousal that enabled him to give his best possible performance. As I shall explain in the next chapter, a certain level of physical and mental arousal is essential to achieve our personal best when confronted by any challenging activity.

Let us now consider a psychological barrier created not as a result of a single traumatic childhood experience but through the harrowing daily experiences of a young girl brought up by a domineering, critical and insensitive father. It is the story of an intelligent and ambitious woman whose happiness and self-confidence were blighted by an inability to stand up to a bullying and over-bearing husband.

Jacquie – Ambitious Executive and Domestic Doormat

Jacquie, a bright and ambitious high achiever in her early forties, works as a senior buyer for a major high street retailer. An excellent 'people person' she can be firm without appearing pushy and assertive without ever coming across as aggressive. While dealing with staff and clients she was always cool, calm and totally in command of events. At home, however, it was a very different story. Friends and relatives were astonished and bewildered at the transformation that took place whenever her front door closed behind her. From being a confident and assertive executive, she allowed herself to be reduced to a state of child-like helplessness by an overbearing bully of a husband. It was he who made all the decisions, usually without even bothering to consult her, and then rode roughshod over any objections she might attempt to raise.

Whenever friends urged Jacquie to stand up for herself she would just shrug, smile and say it was John's way of showing how much he loved her. Rather than provoke a row or, worst fear of all, risk him walking out on her, she was prepared to go along with his demands, no matter how selfish and unreasonable they seemed to outsiders. For over seven years she fell back on the comforting myth that it was his way of demonstrating his deep love for her. Not once during that time, she later confessed to me, had she questioned, or perhaps dared to question, *why* she felt so compelled to accept as normal such bullying arrogance in her private life when she would not have tolerated it for a single moment at work. So what did transform ambitious executive Jacquie into a domestic doormat?

Jacquie's Story

'My father, Eric, might well have been a clone for my husband John,' she told the group. 'His word was law and my mother never questioned his right to make every decision for the family. Until the time I left home at eighteen, to go to university, I meekly accepted that this was how all fathers behaved and that, as a dutiful daughter, I must always fall in line with his demands, respect his wishes, and strive to live up to his high expectations.'

A clever and highly articulate university professor who used withering sarcasm to devastating effect, Eric took a delight in playing word games with his daughter. Like a prosecuting counsel he would lead her into saying things she didn't really mean before pouncing delightedly on any contradictions or logical flaws in her arguments. 'Looking back I can see that every conversation I had with my father was like a game of chess. I knew from the start he would end up by check-mating me and sarcastically shooting my arguments down in flames – it was just a question of how long it took.'

As a result grown-up Jacquie, when dealing with her equally domineering husband John, regressed to that 12-year-old child in the presence of her father. If she ever thought of standing up for herself and challenging his decisions, guilt, anxiety and self-doubt would flood into her mind and paralyse her will. Any desire she might have had to behave differently, to assert her rights as an individual and to demand a genuine say in decisions that affected both of them, was blocked by memories of her childhood relationship with her father.

Jacquie's Therapy

The starting point for transforming doormat Jacquie into the same assertive and self-confident career woman she became at work was to teach her first to build greater 'core stability' (see Part Two: Chapter Eleven: Procedure One) to provide a better basis for the breathwork training that followed.

Core stability refers to the strength of those muscles that form the walls of the abdomen, sides and back directly beneath the rib cage.

These can be strengthened by means of four easily followed, non-strenuous exercises, and Jacquie was asked to spend six minutes each day working with them.

At the same time she was taught deep diaphragmatic breathing followed by training with the relaxing breath and Breakthrough Breathwork. Finally we were ready to proceed with a series of intense and, initially, somewhat distressing sensualizations.

As Jacquie's father had died two years earlier I decided to arrange a 'meeting' between the two of them. We started with her entering the mountainside tunnel at the end of which she found three doors, one on the left, one on to the right and the third directly ahead reached by a short flight of stone stairs. I guided her up these steps and through the door at the top. I always allow my clients to sensualize any type of door they prefer, and in this case she selected an iron bound wooden one of the sort you might find in an old castle or baronial hall. As the door 'swung open' Jacquie found herself in a huge chamber filled with the most brilliant light. Here in this place of peace and light Jacquie 'met' her late father. In her mind's eye she not only 'saw' him but also heard his familiar rather rasping voice, smelled the stale pipe tobacco that always hung around his head like a halo and even embraced him.

Although this procedure may strike you as macabre and distressing in the extreme, it is in fact an excellent and insightful way of assisting clients whose progress through life is being blocked by having unfinished business with a departed loved one. Over a period of several sessions, and despite some slight early misgivings, Jacquie rapidly developed a strong and vivid sensualization involving her dead father and even looked forward to their weekly 'meetings'. During therapy Jacquie was encouraged to 'tell' her father how much she had resented his overbearing manner and how, paradoxically, this had led her to choose a husband whose manner was almost identical.

In time her father 'apologized' to her for his unreasonable behaviour for the first time. It arose, he 'explained', from a deep – if never openly expressed – love for his only child and a desire to prepare her for what he believed to be a cruel and dangerous world. Let me make it perfectly clear that I am not for one moment suggesting that the ghost of her father appeared before her. All that he 'said' to her, including his 'apology' and 'explanation', were created entirely from Jacquie's own imagination. We can never know whether, subconsciously, she had always believed that a deep love underlay his behaviour, or indeed whether this was the truth of the matter. But, as with Jason, what mattered was that Jacquie believed this to be the truth and, in coming to her realization, changed her emotional response towards her father. It was the breakthrough that allowed her to move forward with her life.

Later in her sensualizations Jacquie was invited to 'meet' her living husband John in a similar way, this time not in an underground chamber but in different rooms around their own home. During these encounters she was to practise standing up to him, disagreeing where appropriate with his ideas and opinions, and assertively expressing her own viewpoint. Once again we started with small, even trivial, disagreements before working up to major sources of conflict between them.

Although difficult and painful at first these confrontations became increasingly easy for her to manage, until a point was reached at which she felt sufficiently strong emotionally to put them into practice in real life. It was not an easy process and it was one which John resisted every step of the way. In the end, to her relief, unable to tolerate the new, assertive and independent-minded Jacquie, he stormed out. To her surprise she discovered that, far from being emotionally devastated by the ending of their relationship, as she had always dreaded, she was actually delighted to see the back of him and move forward with her life.

A few months later she met a gentle, affectionate man as unlike her former partner as it was possible to be. At the time of writing they have moved to France and are still living happily together in a small stone farmhouse near the beautiful hilltop town of Fayence, not far from where this book is being written.

What These Case Histories Tell Us

These two reports illustrate just a few of the many ways in which mental and physical barriers to personal progress can develop, and some of the ways in which they prevent us achieving all that we want to achieve and would otherwise be capable of accomplishing in life.

In the last chapter I said that the normally accepted sequence of events by which these psychological barriers to performance occurs is, using the case of Jason as an example, as follows:

1. As he prepares to speak, Jason begins to experience anxiety.
2. He becomes painfully aware that his heart is racing, his mouth is dry, his stomach is churning and he is starting to breathe erratically.
3. Waves of panic sweep over him. He cannot think clearly or speak coherently.

But this, as I pointed out, is not really what is going on. The actual sequence of events in every case of a performance-zapping emotional response — whether fear, anger or even indifference — is explained below.

Our pattern of breathing changes under the influence of a region of the brain, known as the limbic system, which I shall describe in detail in Chapters Four and Five. This part of the brain, which functions below our normal level of conscious awareness, not only regulates our emotional reactions to events, especially those connected with the well-known 'fight or flight' response, but is also responsible for laying down memories.

Whenever we experience a significant event in our lives — whether painful or pleasant — the limbic system orchestrates an automatic mental and physical response. This includes instructing the relatively small body of cells in the nearby respiratory centre to change the pattern of breathing according to the demands of the situation.

The limbic system also 'tags' that event in long-term memory, noting not only details of the circumstances but also the associated emotional state *and* the pattern of breathing associated with it. In the future, whenever a situation is perceived as being, in some way, similar to that original event, the same pattern of breathing is triggered. This does two things. First it subtly alters the chemical composition of the blood which in turn stimulates our nervous system. Second it awakens those memories associated with the previous event or events. These changes in the pattern of our breathing then bring about all the other physical and mental changes that lead to deterioration in performance. For this reason I term these barriers breath locks, or b-locks for short, and this is how I shall refer to them in future.

Since all these are happening below our level of awareness it takes a certain amount of time before we become aware that anything is going on or going wrong. So far as we are concerned everything is ticking along nicely. Indeed, when the changes are only slight we may remain blissfully unaware of them. What we do know, however, is that our performance of some task is less good than usual. If playing a competitive sport, for example, we will certainly be aware that we are not performing at the peak of our potential. If trying to concentrate we'll find our mind starting to wander. If attempting to remember something, our memory will prove uncharacteristically and frustratingly elusive. The chances of failure will increase and we'll probably tell ourselves we are having an 'off day'.

Should mental and physical arousal increase beyond a certain critical point, however, we will start to become all too well aware of these unhelpful feelings and thoughts. In the usual scenario for explaining strong emotions, therefore, changes in our breathing are viewed as the consequences rather than the cause of these changes.

In my Breakthrough Breathwork programme (Part Two), by contrast, I consider b-locks to be the primary cause of deteriorating performance and failure. Just as all life starts with a breath so, too, do most of the psychological difficulties we experience and the barriers to personal progress that we encounter. There are in fact six different ways that the pattern of breathing can alter, and varying degrees to which these changes take place.

- **Depth of breathing** – can be deep or shallow or anywhere between the two extremes.
- **Rate of breathing** – may be fast, slow or somewhere between the two. By a fast breath I mean in excess of 20 inhalations and exhalations per minute and by slow I mean as few as two in 60 seconds. A rate of between 12 and 17 is usually considered 'normal'.
- **Texture of breathing** – ranges from smooth and even to erratic and uneven.
- **Length of breathing** – are your inhalations and exhalations of a similar duration or is one noticeably longer or shorter than the other? Differences in breath length are not necessarily a bad thing or a sign of dysfunctional breathing – indeed such variations form the basis for several of the procedures you will learn in Part Two. But where they occur you can expect to find similar changes in the way your brain and body respond.
- **Location of breathing** – may take place low down in the body or high up in the chest. Again the part of your anatomy from which you breathe plays an important role in levels of mental and physical arousal.
- **Quality of breathing** – can be laboured and effortful, as when trying to catch one's breath after overly vigorous exertion, or so effortless that it occurs without your being consciously aware of the fact.

Given that each one of these six can vary widely, as can the interactions between them, it is easy to see how complex and diverse the changes in our patterns of breathing can quickly become.

Major changes, such as when we pant from exertion, fear or anger are apparent to everyone, as is the gasping, shallow breathing characteristic of hyperventilation. However, even the slightest variations in the rate and depth of our breathing can prove sufficient to undermine our performance in a wide range of activities. In many instances these variations may be so slight and subtle that we remain unaware they are even occurring, and do not recognize their negative effects on performance. This is because it often requires only a relatively minor increase or, less usually, decrease in our level of mental and physical arousal to shift us out of what sports psychologists term our Zone of Optimal Individual Functioning, and which I refer to as our O-Zone.

In the next chapter I shall be describing exactly what this zone is and explaining how to monitor your position on the 'performance arousal curve' so as discover whether you are at your optimal level of functioning for any particular activity.

In summary, Breakthrough Breathwork involves these six key ideas:

1. We learn, perhaps as the result of a single traumatic event, as in the case of Jason, or over a long period of time, as with Jacquie, to associate some powerful emotional state with a particular pattern of breathing. This creates a b-lock that acts as a barrier to performance.

2. Sometimes we know, or believe we know, what caused the b-lock in the first place, as well as the circumstances most likely to undermine our performance. On other occasions we may have repressed the memory of the event that originally led to a b-lock. In such cases it is usually necessary to get to the root of the problem, or else one ends up merely treating the symptoms rather than eliminating their cause.

3. In any situation that either is, or is perceived to be, similar to that in which the b-lock was established, the limbic system of the brain instructs the respiratory centre to switch to the same pattern

of breathing. Because this occurs below our level of normal awareness we are seldom aware of what is happening until it is too late.

4. The change in breathing, by affecting the delicate chemical balance of the blood and through emotional associations within the limbic system, triggers the fight or flight response.

5. At this point mind and body start switching into a highly aroused survival mode in preparation for fighting or fleeing.

6. Even when the subsequent mental and physical arousal remains at a low level it can still prove sufficient to disrupt our performance by moving us away from our O-Zone.

In the next chapter I will explain exactly what the O-Zone is and how you can plot your own for any recent activity.

CHAPTER THREE

Welcome to your O-Zone

'Acquiring the appropriate skills for voluntarily controlling unwanted anxiety and arousal is an important part of developing your mental game plan. These skills will enable you to reduce arousal levels when you're feeling over-anxious and to increase arousal when you're not feeling pumped up enough.'
STEPHEN J. BULL – THE MENTAL GAME PLAN

We have all been in situations where we badly wanted to achieve some important life goal only to have success snatched from our grasp. Frequently the most frustrating and tantalizing aspect of such failures is our certain knowledge that we are perfectly capable of achieving our ambitions. We know we have it within ourselves to triumph. We may even have succeeded in the recent past, yet on this occasion we manage to snatch defeat from the jaws of victory and are left reflecting miserably on how badly we have let both ourselves, and those who had faith in us, down.

Almost everyone suffers from such disappointing setbacks from time to time. Indeed the more ambitious and hard working we are the greater our chances of experiencing such failures to achieve our true potential. So what is it that prevents us from *consistently* performing at the peak of our knowledge, skills and experience, and what practical steps can we take to ensure we can always do so?

These are questions that I am frequently asked by the athletes with whom I have worked. These self-disciplined and highly skilled competitors have a very clear idea of exactly what they are capable of achieving – on a good day. That is a day when they attain, or even exceed, their personal best; occasions when they shave a few fractions of a second off their time, jump a little higher, lift a little more weight or hit the ball more accurately and powerfully than ever before. When things go wrong they, and we, often put it down to just a 'bad day', do our best to shrug off the disappointment and fervently hope to do better the next time. While perfectly understandable, this explanation neither helps identify the cause of our difficulties nor, more importantly, suggests a practical strategy for avoiding similar setbacks on subsequent occasions.

Before we look at why we all experience bad and good days, let's consider the common factor linking in all human endeavours, whether on an athletics track, at work or in our private lives.

The Game of Life is Played on a 14-Centimetre Pitch!

The connection between challenges as seemingly disparate as running a major company and going for gold at the Olympics is simply this: every game in life is played on a 14-centimetre-wide pitch – the distance between your ears.

Take, for example, the challenge of the four-minute mile. For decades athletes had been striving, without success, to run that distance in 240 seconds or less. In 1945 the world record time of 4 minutes 1.3 seconds was achieved by the Swedish runner Gunter Hagg, and for almost a decade it remained unbroken. Indeed many coaches and athletes were convinced that this represented the ultimate limit of human physical ability and so could never be bettered. Then, on 6 May 1954, at an athletics meeting in Oxford, Roger Bannister, a 25-year-old medical student from St Mary's Hospital Medical School in London, completed the distance in 3 minutes 59.4 seconds, so setting a new world record.

The following year more than thirty top class runners accomplished the same feat and within a few years hundreds had done so, many of them ordinary enthusiasts rather than élite athletes. By smashing the record for the four-minute mile Roger Bannister did more than break through an apparent physical barrier. No less importantly he demolished an even more potent psychological barrier as well.

With this crucial psychological aspect clearly in mind we'll return to our consideration of why we have good days and bad days, and look at what can be done to transform every attempt into achievement by banishing bad days from our life forever.

Your Zone of Optimal Individual Functioning

Research by Finnish sports psychologist Yuri Hannin has established that to perform at peak efficiency we have to remain within what he terms our Zone of Optimal Individual Functioning (O-Zone). The illustration on page 41 shows this zone and its position on what is called the arousal curve. If we move to the right of the O-Zone we become overly anxious and agitated to perform at our best. The further we drift in this direction the more rapidly our performance declines as anxiety turns into panic, as the following case history clearly illustrates:

Susan – Melting Under Pressure

Blonde, petite and highly talented Susan is a young skater of such potential that some experts believe she has it in her to win Olympic Gold. On present performance, however, she is unlikely even to gain third place in a minor league contest.

Now aged twenty, Susan has been skating since she was seven and is being coached by a former UK national champion. Five times a week she and her parents rise at five in the morning to drive the sixty miles between her home and the nearest ice rink that offers professional training facilities. There, before the public is admitted, she practises under the watchful eye of her coach and the anxious gaze of her mother and father. Under these conditions she usually skates superbly well, skimming across the ice and performing even the most complex and elaborate routines with the grace and skill of a consummate professional. In a competition, however, it is usually a very different story.

'I melt under pressure,' Susan admits. 'As soon as I step out onto the ice I can feel my heart start to race, my legs begin to tremble and my co-ordination becomes slow and clumsy.'

Susan's Story

Whenever she steps onto the ice in a major contest, Susan takes two other people with her – Mum and Dad. They sit inside her head watchful and critical, a constant and constantly nagging reminder of all they have sacrificed to get her to where she is now.

'I am very aware of how much time, money and effort it has cost Mum and Dad to support me in my skating,' she said. 'Each time I compete I worry about letting them down.'

It is, of course, a self-fulfilling prophecy. The more she worries, the more anxious Susan becomes. The greater her anxiety the less capable she is of skating at her peak level of ability. The saddest thing about this is that neither of her parents has even raised the matter, complained about the 'burden' she imagines her skating has imposed on them or done other than be entirely supportive. It is more a matter of what Susan *believes* may be going through their minds than their actual thoughts and feelings.

In this case it is easy to see how these worries and anxieties, which come to the fore under competitive pressures, move Susan away from her O-Zone and down the right side of her arousal curve. This causes her performance to deteriorate sharply while her desperate struggle to regain form only causes her to skate less and less well, until another defeat becomes inevitable. It is a similar problem to that facing Jason when he had to make a presentation, and Jacquie when she attempted to stand up to her bullying husband. In all these cases arousal increases to the point where performance has nowhere to go but downwards.

While rising levels of mental and physical arousal are often to blame for a decline in performance, this is not always the case. There may also be a shift to the left of the curve leading to a loss of confidence, motivation and a desire to succeed. The individual becomes lethargic, loses focus and concentration and simply gives up all attempts to succeed. What frequently happens is a pendulum effect, first a swing to the right of the curve followed by an equally sharp swing back to the left. An initial increase in arousal leads to an inability to perform some important activity effectively. Successive failure then leads to depression and a loss of interest in even attempting that task, a condition that is sometimes described as 'learned helplessness'. On many occasions the swing occurs fairly slowly over a period of weeks or months, but it can also occur with dramatic suddenness, as the next case history shows.

Martin – A House-Bound House Agent

A healthy man in his late thirties, Martin woke up one morning and found himself incapable of getting out of bed – not because there was anything physically wrong but because, virtually overnight so it seemed to him, he had developed a terror of doing so. This is a condition known as agoraphobia, an intense fear not, as many believe, of open spaces but of places where others are present (from the Greek *agora*, meaning 'market place').

Martin's Story

Until that terrified awakening Martin had always considered himself physically fit and emotionally well balanced, although he also admitted to being under a high level of stress. This had started some nine months earlier when the family-owned estate agency, for which he had worked since leaving school, was taken over by a far more dynamic and ruthless company. The relaxed regime to which he had become accustomed was replaced by early starts and late finishes. There was intense pressure from an aggressive new manager to achieve ever more demanding and – in Martin's view – unrealistic sales targets.

'Ever since school I have always had problems with authority figures,' he told me. 'I went to a private school where they still used corporal punishment. The prospect of being beaten so terrified me that I was desperately well behaved as a child. On a number of occasions, however, my entire class was beaten for the behaviour of a couple of disruptive lads who never owned up to their misdeeds. Since it was against the code of honour to sneak on them we were all expected to accept a beating.

'The class had to line up to bend over and get six strokes from a cane or gym slipper with all the others watching. I can remember the sickening dread in my stomach as the line ahead of me got shorter and shorter, until it was my turn to touch my toes. My heart would be racing and I could hardly breathe. The fear and nausea I experienced while awaiting my punishment was far, far worse than the actual pain inflicted.'

After three such incidents, Martin inadvertently developed an effective avoidance strategy. Before his turn came around he genuinely fainted. 'I dropped like a stone, gashing my head open on the edge of a desk. I woke up in the sanatorium with the school nurse mopping up blood from a scalp wound. This made the masters think twice before beating me again, and although I got teased by the other boys I escaped further punishment.'

Martin's confrontational new manager, although a year his junior, reminded him of being back in school. 'He managed to awaken all those old fears and feelings in me. Being called into his office for a dressing down reminded me of the beatings I received, through no fault of my own, in class.'

On the morning he woke up too terrified to leave home he was, in a sense, repeating his fainting fit in class. 'I felt under increasing and unbearable pressure,' Martin admitted when he had finally gained sufficient motivation and mobility to visit my consulting room. 'Even so, I believed I was coping adequately, and that so much stress was an unavoidable part of modern living.'

Had he been much older and less fit, that intense stress might have triggered a physical breakdown. As it was he became first intensely anxious and then deeply depressed. He lost all interest in his career or even in caring for himself at the most basic level. Fortunately he had an understanding wife who took charge, supported and encouraged him and, after a few months, finally persuaded him to seek psychological help for his problems.

The O-Zone of Opportunity

While we remain within our O-Zone we can perform to the very best of our ability, experience and training. We approach challenges positively and with a very high confidence of success. We remain so clearly focused and free from self-doubt that the performance itself seems almost effortless and the outcome frequently exceeds our most optimistic expectations. Later we may describe ourselves as having been 'on peak form' and explain it away by saying 'everything just clicked', or 'I really got my act together'. We may also wonder, perhaps slightly forlornly, why these moments of peak accomplishment are so few and far apart. Wouldn't it be great, we think wistfully, if I could *always* perform as well as that when it really mattered. The good news is that we all have it within ourselves to do just that.

Discovering Your Own O-Zone

As the illustration below shows, insufficient mental and physical arousal undermines performance because we lack the necessary motivation and drive to achieve the goal. We feel too laid back or indifferent to the outcome to try our best. The further to the left of the curve we are the less concerned or interested we are in success.

Too much arousal, by contrast, will cause performance to decline sharply, as increasing anxiety leads to self-doubt, uncertainty and confusion. You lose focus and find your body failing to carry out even well practised activities much less confidently than before. This moves you out of the O-Zone towards the right of the curve. The greater our level of arousal the faster performance declines. By mental and physical arousal I mean the varying levels of alertness, motivation, energy and involvement that can be focused on the task at hand.

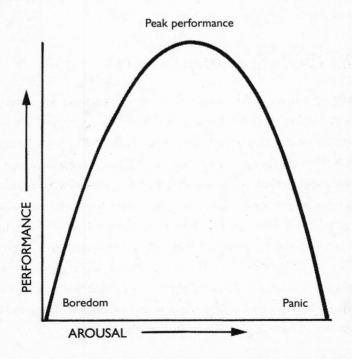

Plotting Your Performance/Arousal Curves

At this point I'd like you to stop reading and think about three recent activities. First recall one in which you failed to function at peak potential because you were too far to the left of the graph.

* Reflect on your feelings as well as your performance.
* Were you bored, apathetic, disinterested or tired?
* How did these negative feelings effect things such as concentration, hand-eye co-ordination, creativity, problem solving skills, persistence, mental focus, etc?
* If you were listening to your inner voice what sort of things was it saying to you?

Place an X on the graph on page 43 at a point that approximates to your level of performance. The position of this mark also reveals your probable level of physical and mental arousal on that occasion.

Next recall an occasion at which you failed to achieve your true potential because you were too far over to the right of the graph. As before, reflect on your emotions in that situation.

* Were you overly apprehensive, anxious, fearful or panicky?
* How did these negative emotions affect your performance?
* Did your self-confidence take a knock? Did you find it impossible to stay focused, to concentrate and recover from a setback?
* If you heard an inner voice, what was it saying to you?

Place an X on the graph to indicate your level of performance.
Finally, consider a time when everything really clicked and you performed at the peak of your true potential.

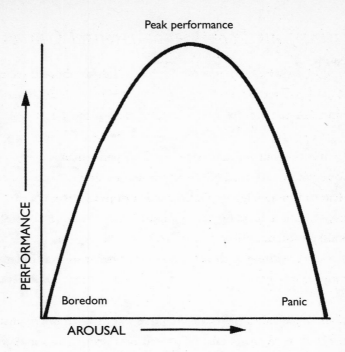

Peak performance

PERFORMANCE

Boredom

Panic

AROUSAL

This exercise is useful because it helps to bring to the forefront of your mind both the negative and positive consequences that follow differing levels of arousal. In the next chapter we'll be exploring the arousal curve further as I describe how moving out of their O-Zone significantly and adversely affected the lives and careers of four of my recent clients.

Summary of Chapters One–Three

* While changes in breathing are often seen as the consequences of increasing levels of mental and physical arousal, this is not the case. Rather they are the trigger for these further changes, the spark that lights the gunpowder trail and not one of the effects of the subsequent detonation.

* Even small changes in the depth or rate of breathing are sufficient to bring about profound and potentially catastrophic changes to levels of arousal.

- This occurs as the result of b-locks developing, often below our normal level of awareness.
- Our ability to perform any challenging task depends on remaining within our personal O-Zone, which varies from one individual to the next, and one activity to another.
- In every case a shift away from our O-Zone — in either direction — leads to a sharp decline in our ability to perform at the peak of our true potential.
- The further we move to either the left or the right of the O-Zone the worse our performance becomes.
- What we call 'good days', therefore, mean those occasions when we remained within the O-Zone when carrying out a particular task. Equally, 'bad days' indicate a shift to the left or right of the zone.

Having seen what happens we now need to examine why it happens. In the next two chapters I will describe an area of the brain which, although long ignored by researchers, is now recognized to be of vital importance to our success and happiness. It is here, in this ancient region, that not only our most powerful feelings, emotions and motives arise but also any blocks that prevent us achieving our true potential.

Of necessity these are somewhat technical chapters and you may feel you would sooner skip ahead to Chapter Six, where I consider breathing and the mechanisms by which we take a breath. While knowledge of what follows will provide you with helpful insights into the way b-locks originate it is not essential for a proper understanding of the practical procedures taught in Part Two.

CHAPTER FOUR

Your three-part brain

'It is mental power that separates the exceptional from the very good. What separates them is what goes on behind the eyes.'
FRANK DICK OBE, FORMER COACH TO GREAT BRITAIN'S TRACK AND FIELD TEAM

Clench your fists and place them together with the fingers touching and you will have an approximation of the size and shape of the human brain. This organ, which is about the size of a grapefruit, weighs around 1500 g (3 lb), comprises only 2 per cent of body weight and yet consumes 20 per cent of our total energy output, may be likened to a very old house onto which different generations have added new storeys. The result is what neuroanatomist Paul MacLean, a researcher at the National Institute of Mental Health at Poolesville, Maryland, has called the 'triune' brain, triune because it consists of three distinctly different assemblies of nerve cells, each in turn revealing, anatomically and chemically, common ancestry with reptiles, early mammals and late mammals (see illustration over the page). Each of the three has its own radically different structure and chemistry, its own evolutionary history, its own type of intelligence, its own specialized memory and the capacity to function independently of the other two.

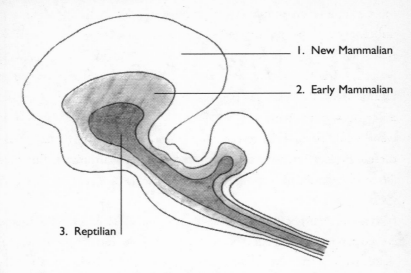

1. New Mammalian
2. Early Mammalian
3. Reptilian

The Lowest Level – Your Reptilian Brain

The oldest of the three structures, it evolved more than 500 million years ago, and resembles the complete brain of modern-day reptiles. For this reason it is known as the 'reptilian' brain. Pull apart your clenched fist, still keeping your wrists pressed closely together, and the part directly above and extending slightly down your wrists roughly approximates to this part of the brain. Here you will find those clusters of cells responsible for levels of alertness, as well as so-called 'vegetative' functions such as regulating heartbeat and controlling breathing.

The Highest Level – Your New Mammalian Brain

Known as the neo-cortex, this level comprises those 'little grey cells' so beloved of Hercule Poirot. Although not especially large, if flattened out the cells would cover only some four sheets of A4 paper. This, the most recent addition to the brain, is still the seat of reason and consciousness.

The neo-cortex is divided into two hemispheres with the left (in most people) containing centres responsible for both speaking and understanding speech as well as for logical, analytical thought. The right hemisphere, although it has some language capabilities, is generally viewed as being more involved with imagination, fantasy and intuition. In the past people became extremely excited by these differences, with many psychologists and others making claims that went wildly beyond the research evidence. Today we know that, while these different functions certainly exist, the two hemispheres function far more as a unified whole than as two separate brains within one skull.

The neo-cortex is also responsible for our sense of self – the image we possess of what we look like. Such self-recognition, an ability we share with some apes, is considered to be the hallmark of self-awareness. While our reptilian brain is essential for survival and the neo-cortex enables us to function as human beings, the expression of our individuality, as well as our capacity to achieve our true potential, crucially depends on that middle layer, situated like meat in a sandwich between the other two.

The Middle Region – Your Early Mammalian Brain

In 1878 a French surgeon called Paul Broca named this area of the brain the 'great limbic lobe' because it *surrounds* (from the Latin *limbus* meaning a border) the reptilian brain. Seventy-four years later Paul MacLean proposed that these structures be renamed the limbic system. Within this region emotions are generated, sexual drive and performance are determined, memories are placed into long-term storage, and incoming information is emotionally tagged before being directed to other regions of the brain for further processing. Here too are orchestrated the complex hormonal and behavioural responses that, in the face of a perceived threat, combine to produce the well-known fight, flight or freeze reaction. This link between memory and emotion is extremely significant in terms of creating blocks to our potential, for the more emotionally charged an event the greater is the likelihood that it will be remembered clearly and vividly. In a study that examined the relationship between retention, recall and emotions, subjects were shown gruesome photographs of accident victims and instructed to keep their emotions in check while doing so. When later tested on specific details of the pictures they did less well than a control group who had been allowed to respond emotionally to the injuries.

This region of the brain says Jean-Didier Vincent, Professor of Neurophysiology at the University of Bordeaux, is: 'Like the limbo of Christian mythology…the intermediary between the neocortical heaven and the reptilian hell.'

Paul Broca himself was so convinced that the limbic system functions at an animal level, its responses controlled not by rational thought but by raw feelings, that he described it as the '*cerveau brutal*' (brutal brain) in contrast with the '*cerveau intellectual*' or intellectual brain. Because the limbic system is strongly connected to the olfactory bulb, responsible for our sense of smell, Broca speculated that its chief function was in interpreting odours. Since smell was not considered of any great significance in humans the entire limbic system was dismissed as being of little or no importance, given no more than a passing reference in most text-books and barely mentioned in medical school. As recently as forty years ago, one anatomist commented that it had: … probably not contributed greatly to the evolution of the human brain and will … not be considered further.' It was, in the words of Paul MacLean, 'treated like an unwanted child in the teaching of brain anatomy.'

It was not until 1937 that the American neuroanatomist James Wenceslas Papez made the link between the limbic system and human emotions. Following up this idea some ten years later, MacLean speculated that no real dialogue was possible between it and higher regions of thought since the system: ' … eludes the grasp of the intellect because its animalistic and primitive structure makes it impossible to communicate in verbal terms.' He concluded that while intellectual reasoning and logical analysis occur in the most recent and most highly developed portions of the brain, our emotional behaviour is dominated by this 'relatively crude and primitive system, leading to a difference between what we 'feel' and what we 'know'' between gut instinct and objective inference.

The importance of the long neglected limbic system in determining almost every aspect of our daily life and human experience can be judged by the fact that recent studies have suggested it is within this area of the brain that religious experiences arise. One of the leading researchers to make this claim is Andrew Newberg, a neuroscientist at the University of Pennsylvania in Philadelphia. Together with a colleague, the late Eugene d'Aquili, Dr Newberg set out to explore what Albert Einstein described as a sense of 'oneness with the universe', the sensation of profound awe and unity that results from a religious experience which is common to people of all faiths.

For their first study Newberg and d'Aquili found eight skilled Buddhist meditators who agreed to undergo brain imaging once they had achieved a deeply meditative state by means of focusing intently on a religious symbol. In this state of mind one's everyday sense of the self disappears. In the words of one of their volunteers: 'It's as if the film of your life broke and you were seeing the light that allowed the film to be projected.'

The imaging technique used by Newberg and his colleague, known as Single Photon Emission Computed Tomography (SPECT), enabled them to produce a snapshot of activity in the meditator's brain just at the moment their sense of self dissolved and they experienced the sensation of oneness with the universe.

Later the same researchers conducted a similar experiment with Franciscan nuns when they were deep in prayer. In both studies they observed a reduction of activity in those areas of the brain concerned with regulating attention. 'When you look at people in meditation they really do turn off their sensations to the outside world,' says Newberg. 'Sights and sounds don't disturb them any more.'

But there was far more to this experience than the deep sense of separation between 'self' and 'other'. Even more striking was a feeling that the experience was immensely significant combined with overwhelming awe. These powerful emotions, the brain imaging showed, originated within the primitive limbic system. An important part of this system's job is to label certain events that have particular personal significance. Increased activity in this region, many scientists believe, causes it to tag some events as highly significant. This would help to explain why it is virtually impossible to communicate this experience of ecstatic bliss to others. 'The components of the experience – the visual components, the sensory components – are just the same as everyone else experiences them all the time,' points out Jeffrey Saver, a neurologist at UCLA. 'Instead the temporolimbic system is stamping these moments as being intensely important to the individual, as being characterized by great joy and harmony. When the experience is reported to someone else, only the content and the sense that it's different can be communicated. The visceral sensation can't.'

The fact that all religions make use of ritual, Newberg points out, is more than a coincidence. Many of the shared aspects of those rituals, such as music, a particular place or building in which to conduct them, and especially stylized chanting and movements, stimulate the limbic system and, by doing so, serve to increase the richness of the experience.

From the perspective of this training programme, the point to bear in mind is that both the movements and, especially, the chanting and singing bring about significant change to the way in which we usually breathe. It is these alterations to the normal pattern of breathing that trigger responses within the limbic system.

Before leaving this topic I should make it clear that while religious sceptics have seized on Newberg's findings to claim it proves that such experiences are 'all in the mind', he himself remains neutral on the implications: 'If you're a religious person,' he comments, 'it makes sense that the brain can do this, because if there is a God, it makes sense to design the brain so that we can have some sort of interaction.'

In the next chapter we shall examine the limbic system's central role both in determining our emotional response to an event and in creating the b-locks that prevent us from being all we want to be and would otherwise be capable of becoming.

CHAPTER FIVE

The limbic system in action

'I discovered that, after a certain point of nervousness, I would start to deteriorate pretty rapidly. There was a real drop-off point in my ability to perform if I got too nervous ... so it was just being able to find that little narrow comfort zone.'
STEVE PODBORSKI, FORMER WORLD DOWNHILL SKI-CHAMPION

Imagine you are walking through the woods when a bear suddenly rears up in front of you. Before you are even consciously aware of that danger an image of the bear rapidly passes from your eyes to structures within the limbic system, where a series of commands is instantly sent to your body which bring about a complex series of physiological changes. Your heart starts to beat faster as your blood pressure rises. You begin to breathe more rapidly. The effect is to move more oxygenated blood rapidly around the body to feed those cells upon whose efforts life or death may depend. At the same time this blood is directed away from your skin (which is why we go pale and clammy from fear) and sent to your brain and skeletal muscles in readiness to fight or flee. The muscle food glycogen is released from your liver to provide your muscles with the energy they will need during intense activity, while more glucose is liberated into the bloodstream to nourish the brain. The time it takes your blood to clot is reduced to minimize the effects of any injury. Meanwhile your digestion closes down since there is little point in expending effort and energy digesting your dinner if it increases the risk of your ending up as someone else's! Like a battleship closing for action stations the body shuts down any functions that are not directly related to survival.

All these changes, directed by the limbic system, occur well before the higher visual centres have even confirmed that the object you have encountered is indeed a bear. This part of the brain is, therefore, continuously processing information below the level of our conscious awareness. This helps explain the familiar 'Aha' experience, that sense of revelation that occurs whenever our conscious mind finally discovers something our subconscious mind has long known.

If you think back over the case histories described earlier, it seems clear that during those moments of childhood trauma their limbic systems tagged those experiences as being deeply significant, and linked them to a particular pattern of breathing. This is hardly surprising since the centre that controls respiration is located within a part of the brain

The Brain

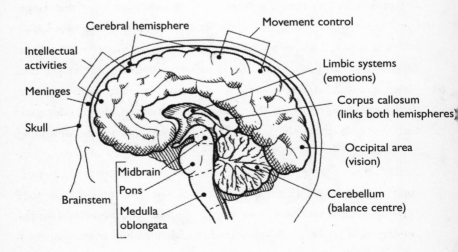

stem known as the medulla oblongata that, as the illustration below shows, is in close proximity to the limbic system. All that was necessary to produce the same painful feelings, and generate the same sense of panic, despair and hopelessness, was for a similar pattern of breathing to be repeated. The result was a dramatic shift away from the O-Zone that resulted in an abrupt and drastic decline in performance.

Before leaving this topic we need to explore one other aspect of brain function — the relationship between our conscious and unconscious minds. Ask most people how they decide to take some action, even something as trivial as bending a finger, and they will say they make a conscious decision that their brain then acts upon by sending nervous impulses to the muscles concerned. Although this seems a matter of simple common sense, research going back more than twenty years clearly demonstrates that it doesn't work like this at all!

Your Conscious and Unconscious Mind

There is startling experimental evidence to show that by the time we 'consciously' decide to perform any action, those areas of the brain lying outside conscious awareness have already sent out the necessary instructions to do so. A striking demonstration of the delay of consciousness was made in 1979 by Professor Benjamin Libet from the Department of Physiology at the University of California in San Francisco. He sat people in a comfortable chair, wired them to an EEG machine, asked them to relax and told them to flex a finger or move their hand whenever they felt like it. At the moment they decided to make the movement, they were to note the position of a moving spot on a clock face before them.

The results were remarkable. Half a second *before* an individual consciously decided to make a move, the EEG showed their brain had produced what is termed a 'readiness potential'. That is, it prepared to fire the train of nerve impulses that would cause the muscles of the finger or hand to contract. Conscious awareness of the intention to contract those muscles did not occur until 0.2 of a second prior to the movement. 'The brain evidently "decides" to initiate or, at the least, prepares to initiate the act at a time before there is any reportable subjective awareness that such a decision has taken place,' commented Benjamin Libet in a paper describing their landmark experiment. 'It is concluded that cerebral initiation even of a spontaneous voluntary act of the kind studied here can and usually does begin unconsciously.'

Later, expanding on the implications of his research, he further explained: 'The performance of every conscious voluntary act is preceded by special unconscious cerebral processes that begin about 500 ms (0.5 of a second) or so before the act.'

In other words, far from consciously deciding to act and then carrying out the action, it appears that a consciousness intention follows a decision that has been made below the level of awareness.

No less striking were the results of later experiments, in which by placing electrodes directly on the brains of fully-conscious patients a neurosurgeon enabled Libet to demonstrate that consciousness, too, is subject to a delay of around half a second. This dramatic discovery was made possible by the fact that, because the brain itself cannot feel pain, some types of surgery can be – and indeed have to be – performed with the patient wide awake. Although a local anaesthetic is used to deaden the pain while the top of a skull is removed, the sedated patient is still able to converse with the operating team and answer questions put by them.

By stimulating the brain electrically Libet was able to show that 500 thousandths of a second passed before his volunteers became aware of and reported the stimulus. Even more remarkable was his discovery, made by stimulating both the skin and the brain simultaneously, that the brain then takes a half-second step back in time in order to eliminate subjective awareness of that delay. As Libet put it: 'A competitive runner may start within 100 ms of the starting gun firing, before he is consciously aware of the shot, but would later report having heard the shot before starting.'

So while we may prefer to believe that all our important actions result from a conscious decision to behave in a certain way this is almost certainly not the case. In fact, despite most people's firm conviction to the contrary, our conscious self actually exerts little or no power over how we feel at any given moment or the decision we make as a result of those feelings. There are two reasons for this. Firstly we take in far more information in, literally, the blink of an eye than we can ever be consciously aware of. Secondly the amount of information on which the conscious brain – in other words 'us' – can take in during any given period of time is infinitesimally minute compared to the vast quantities of sensory data processed by the whole of the brain.

In his book *The User Illusion*, Danish writer Tor Norretsranders offers the following intriguing experiment that well illustrates the first barrier to total conscious awareness. Below you will find a simple experiment that he suggests to experience this new level of awareness for yourself.

Exploring Your Instant Imagery

In a moment look away from this page and close your eyes. Now open them again for a fraction of a second, as if your eyelids were the shutters of a camera. Close your eyes again and try to recapture what you saw. Do this now.

You'll find that with only a little practice you become skilled at 'seeing' the images gathered in that brief moment in considerable detail and with good accuracy.

This experiment demonstrates a key point in our understanding of what it means to be consciously aware. In any one wink of the eyes we 'see' far more than we are actually aware of. While focused on the scenes around us we actually take in only a tiny proportion of what the eyes are really seeing. 'Consciousness works slowly,' says Tor. 'It takes time to identify the various objects we have observed in a single glimpse ... more happens in your head than you know, unless you stop and think about it.' The second problem has to do with 'bandwidth', that is the total amount of information a system can receive during any particular period of time.

Half a century ago, Karl Kupfmuller, a professor at the technical university in Darmstadt, set about measuring and comparing what goes into the brain and what comes out of it using a unit that will be familiar to many who use computers – the 'bit', which stands for 'binary digit'.

For the purposes of this discussion, exactly how a 'bit' is calculated does not matter since the difference between the amount of information that our brain takes in each second and the amount of which we are consciously aware speaks for itself.

Kupfmuller estimated that although as many as 100 million bits per second enter our brain, via the eyes, ears and nose, and from receptors within the different organs of our body, we can only be aware of, at most, 45 bits per second. Others believe that the bandwidth of consciousness could be as low as 16 bits/second.

The narrowness of this bandwidth reveals that our much vaunted conscious awareness of, and control over, the world around us is, in the striking phrase of Alan Kay, a computer scientist formerly with the Rank Xerox Research Centre, largely a 'user illusion'. Since, by definition, we can only be aware of those thoughts about which we are consciously aware, they not surprisingly give rise to a belief that what we know about represents the sum total of all there is to know.

A more accurate description of consciousness, however, is to liken it to the Public Relations Officer of a major company called upon to explain our words and deeds to a sceptical and sometimes hostile outside world. We strive to throw the best possible light on our actions despite having only incomplete, highly subjective and frequently inaccurate information. This means that how we view the world emotionally is, on most occasions, as much a product of subjective feelings as objective reality. As the Austrian psychiatrist Alfred Adler commented: 'It is very obvious that we are influenced not by 'facts' but by our interpretation of facts.'

This means that in order to break through the barriers that come between us and the person we want to be and know we can become, it may first be necessary to see the situation from a different perspective. But in order to achieve this new way of looking at challenges it is usually also essential to change our spontaneous physical response to the event – that is to eliminate the b-lock that stands between us and the expression of our true potential.

The Mind-Body Relationship

Although we tend to think of mind and body as being distinct and almost separate entities not the case. Far from being merely a means of transporting and nurturing the brain, our body is in fact an extension of it with everything that happens even at the extremities affecting the manner and efficiency with which it functions.

If you doubt that statement, try to focus on an intellectual challenge while suffering from a raging toothache, or to concentrate on solving a problem after stubbing your big toe! In fact that brain-body link is even more subtle and complex than those examples suggest. The slightest tension in a muscle group or even a minor alteration in the chemistry of our blood can exert an equally powerful effect. When the muscles are needlessly tensed, therefore, the non-rational limbic system, receiving a constant flow of nerve impulses reporting this tension, may 'conclude' that there is an objective threat to our survival and so trigger the fight or flight response for no apparent reason.

The link between muscle tension and changes in our breathing is equally important. Test this for yourself by suddenly clenching one hand into a fist and noting what happens. You will almost certainly notice that at the instant you tensed your muscles you also held your breath. As we shall see in the next chapter even a momentary change in our breathing provokes a significant alteration in our blood chemistry and, as a result, in our level of mental and physical arousal. This means that long before an individual becomes aware that he, or she, is becoming anxious or upset, unconscious processes start to bring about the mental and physical changes associated with those emotional states. This is one reason why simply telling yourself to calm down, not to panic and to focus on remaining relaxed seldom works. The system has already been set running and, by the time we become aware of the fact, is too hyped up to be easily brought down again. To use an analogy, the time to apply the brake to a car is while it is still at the top of a cliff, not when it is tumbling towards the beach below.

The second reason why reassuring words have little or no effect in restoring us to the O-Zone is that the region of the brain responsible for emotional arousal, as well as for memory, motivation and many other crucial aspects of performance, cannot understand verbal commands. Trying to calm down an angry or terrified non-English speaker by shouting at him in English is more likely to increase than decrease his emotional state. Similarly, Paul MacLean believed that the intellectual brain cannot communicate in words with the limbic system because they do not speak the same language.

From the age of around four onwards our higher regions of thought in the neocortex become increasingly word dominated as the left hemisphere – housing the language centres in the majority of people – seizes control of our thinking. Most of us analyse events, make plans, seek reasons why things happen, reach our decisions and reflect on experiences by using words. As the philosopher Ludwig Wittgenstein put it: 'The limits of my language are the limits of my world.'

The limbic system, by contrast, works with images. During dreaming sleep the frequently bizarre and inexplicable images we perceive represent the higher regions of thought becoming aware of the visual world of the limbic system. Freud remarked that dreams were 'a royal road to the subconscious.' What he might equally have said is that they are a reflection of activity within the limbic system.

By using sensualizations, we can communicate more directly and easily with the limbic system since we are now speaking the same language. But before it can pay attention to our message the clamour of competing messages must be quietened. Otherwise it is like whispering to a friend while surrounded by a brass band in full flow. To put the brain into a state where it can pay maximum attention to the sensualization we need to find some way of consciously affecting its subconscious processes, and the only way to do this is by using the one pathway that connects the two – our breathing.

Breathing and Brain Function

Most of the time we are unaware of how we are breathing. Respiratory centres in the reptilian brain are constantly monitoring levels of oxygen and carbon dioxide within the blood and adjusting the depth and rate of each breath accordingly. As a result we are able to sit, walk, run and jump confident in the knowledge that the changing oxygen demands of our muscles will be instantly taken care of.

Equally we can, should we wish to do so, take over the controls from this 'automatic pilot' and deliberately vary the manner in which we breathe. We can slow or speed the pace, choose to take air deeply into the lungs or make each breath shallow. We can – up to a point – even stop breathing entirely!

When a b-lock arises, and before our conscious mind is even aware of the impending problem, the limbic system has sent an instruction to the respiratory centres within the reptilian brain to alter the pattern of our breathing. By affecting the balance of carbon dioxide and oxygen within the blood this, in turn, exerts a profound effect on the functioning of our entire nervous system. Other sensors responding to these changes in blood chemistry alert the limbic system, which responds by making further changes in our pattern of breathing. As a result our level of arousal increases and we move rapidly away from our O–Zone. The inevitable decline in performance that follows is, as it were, 'observed' by the conscious mind, negative thoughts arise, self-confidence declines and performance deteriorates still further.

The good news is that since breathing provides the key to performance, and since it can be brought under conscious control, we can equally well use the power of the breath to remain within the critical O–Zone for any particular challenge.

The purpose of the training programme described in Part Two of this book is to provide you with the practical procedures needed to do just that. In the next chapter we shall start to see how these beneficial effects can be realized through a greater understanding of the mechanism on which our existence depends – our breathing.

Summary of Chapters Four and Five

* What we think of as our brain actually comprises three brains, each with specific and specialized functions.
* The most ancient of these structures is concerned with basic bodily functions, such a breathing.
* The most recent structure is concerned with intellectual thought and reasoning.
* In the middle is our emotional or limbic brain, which emotionally tags incoming information.
* While the limbic system exerts a profound influence over our behaviour, the higher regions of thought are not able directly to influence its responses the two do not speak the same language.

- When we fail to perform any task at our true level of potential it is because a barrier – a b-lock – has arisen within the limbic system as a result of an association with a distressing emotion and a change in our pattern of breathing.
- While such barriers cannot usually be removed by logical argument, they may be eliminated through a form of mental rehearsal known as sensualization.
- This proves most powerful when a specific pattern of breathing is first used to place the brain into the most receptive state in which to make these changes.

CHAPTER SIX

Optimal breathing for optimal living

'*Controlling the breath is a prerequisite to controlling the mind and the body.*'
SWAMI RAMA

Sit in a quiet room and listen carefully. What you hear is the sound of life itself – the slow, measured rhythm of your own breathing. The first and last action you will perform on earth.

Focus for a moment on your nostrils and notice the coolness of the air flowing into your body and compare it to the warm moistness felt as it is exhaled. Notice the rise and fall of your chest as you inhale and exhale. This is an action you will repeat between 12 and 14 times a minute if a man and between 14 and 16 times a minute if a woman, amounting to some 20,000 breaths during each 24-hour period, or around half a billion in the average lifetime.

The vast majority of those breaths will have taken place without your ever becoming consciously aware of the fact. As you work and play, eat and drink, sleep and dream, exercise and make love, the flow of air into and away from your body is controlled completely automatically. Indeed, if the airflow was interrupted for more than around four minutes you would suffer irreparable brain damage and probable death.

To Eastern sages, breathing held far greater significance than the mere exchange of gases, essential for survival though this is. *Psyche pneuma* in Greek means breath, soul or spirit. In Latin the phrase *anima spiritus* has a similar meaning of breath or soul. The Japanese express the same idea with their word *ki*, which translates as air or spirit, while in Sanskrit breath is *prana* – the first unit (*pra*) of energy (*na*) – signifying the vital energy of the universe.

According to the Upanishads, ancient yogic texts, *prana* represents the link between mind and body. 'If the mind wants to affect the body,' say Swami Rama and Dr Rudolph Ballentine in their book *Science of Breath*, 'it alters the flow of energy or *prana*. If the body affects the mind, this too is accomplished through an effect on the flow of energy, which in turn has an impact on the mind.'

These ancient ideas are reflected in many of our present-day words and sayings. When startled we say that something 'takes our breath away', we complain of someone 'breathing down our necks' or 'not giving me sufficient breathing space'. We wait with 'bated breath' or 'catch our breath'; we 'breathe a sigh of relief and plead with friends 'not to breathe a word' while we nip out of the office to 'take a breather'!

Our pious exclamation 'bless you', whenever someone sneezes, originates in the belief that our soul momentarily leaves the body during a sneeze. We describe a highly creative individual as 'inspired', those who are involved in a plot 'conspire' or 'breathe together,' and at death we are said to 'expire'.

How Are You Breathing Right Now?

Because breathing normally functions automatically and we take it so much for granted it is tricky to notice minor disruptions to the easy flow of air into and out of our lungs. Consider, for instance, the way you are breathing right now. If seated in an easy chair are you slumping comfortably in your seat? If reading at a desk or table, are you resting your head in your hands and leaning forward over the book? Are your legs crossed?

If so then you are reducing the efficiency with which oxygen reaches your cells and carbon dioxide is removed, because the movement of your diaphragm is being restricted. The effect of this is likely to shift you towards the left side of the arousal curve.

If you now start to breathe more rapidly and less deeply (hyperventilate) you will also change the rate at which these gases pass into and out of your bloodstream, reducing the amount of carbon dioxide present. This increases your level of arousal, moving you towards the right of your O-Zone.

The Mechanisms by Which We Breathe

Although the way in which we breathe is reasonably well known it will be helpful to examine the machinery involved in some detail, since there are many subtle yet crucial aspects of this everyday activity about which many people are unaware.

A clear understanding of the basic principles of respiration, and the subtle interactions between body and brain that result, makes it easier to follow the practical training that follows. It will also assist in understanding what can so easily go wrong and why these problems occur.

The purpose of breathing is, of course, to extract oxygen from the air while removing carbon dioxide and water vapour from the body and expelling them into our surroundings. The illustration over the page shows the airways involved, which include the nose, mouth, windpipe (trachea), bronchi and bronchioles.

Unlike other muscles in the body, such as those in our arms and legs, those involved in breathing have to contract repetitively throughout our life. Fortunately the system is extremely energy-

The Basic Breathing Mechanisms

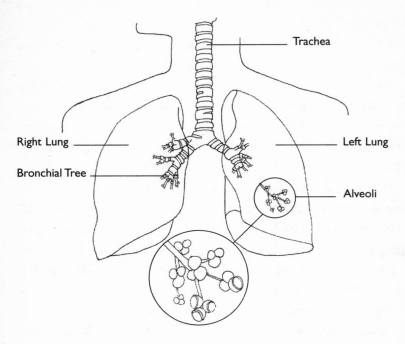

efficient, involving only between 2 and 3 per cent of the body's total expenditure while at rest. Although the rate at which we breathe increases by 15 to 20 times during strenuous exercise, the amount of energy consumed still remains below 4 per cent.

If made to work too hard, however, these muscles can quickly become fatigued, causing us to gasp for air and leading to the rapid increase in mental and physical arousal I mentioned earlier.

While we all use our mouth when gasping for air after a strenuous run or if our nose is blocked by a cold, some people continue doing so even at rest and when their nostrils are free from congestion. This is a bad habit that must be broken if we are to breathe fully and efficiently. To understand why, we need to take a close look at the crucial but insufficiently recognized role of our nose.

Getting Up Your Nose!

The nose acts as an air conditioning plant treating between 5 and 6 litres of air per minute, or the amount present in a small room each day, by purifying, warming and moistening it *en route* to the lungs.

While we tend to think of our nose solely in terms of the fleshy protuberance jutting from the middle of our face, it is much more than that. In fact our external nose – the bit we can see – is uniquely human, being found in no other animal on earth, including our nearest primate relatives.

Their evolutionary role as an air conditioning plant means that noses come in a variety of shapes and sizes, depending on the climate in which a particular race evolved. Those from cool and/or, dry climates have bigger, longer noses to ensure air is effectively warmed and moistened by passing it over a large surface area. People from countries where the air is already warm and moist, by contrast, have wider and more open nostrils.

Our nostrils – known medically as *nares* – derive their name from the Middle English word *thrillen* meaning 'to pierce'. It is the same root from which we get 'to be thrilled', as when we are 'pierced by emotions'. Their function is to shape inhaled air into a fast moving jet stream as it passes into the inner nose. This relatively narrow entrance quickly opens up into a wide nasal passage, the floor of which is formed by the roof of the mouth, or palate.

The front part of the palate is hard and the back soft. You might like to explore your palate now by moving the tip of your tongue from the front teeth as far to the rear of your mouth as you can comfortably manage. Close to the end of its range of movement, you should find the hardness ends and soft, spongy tissue begins. The palate ends in a fleshy, teardrop-shaped piece of muscle, connective tissue and mucus membrane called the *uvula* (Latin for 'little grape'). This lifts to close off the nasal passage whenever we swallow, so helping to prevent food going up our nose.

The roof of the inner nose is also the floor of the brain. Directly above it are the eyes, the optic nerves and the pituitary gland that regulates hormone production. The first cranial nerve, the olfactory nerve that allows us to smell, terminates in the upper part of this nasal passage. When we sniff, whether from enjoyment or disgust, we direct the flow of air upwards towards these nerve endings.

The most obvious structures of the inner nose − we can glimpse them by looking in a mirror − are three bulges known as turbinates. These prominences agitate the incoming air so as to ensure it circulates over as wide an area as possible. Being warm and moist the turbinates prepare incoming air for the delicate tissues in our lungs by heating and humidifying it. Anyone who has found himself fighting to catch his breath on a really cold, dry day will appreciate how vital these bulges are. Although the turbinates become cooler and drier as the outside air passes over them, the passage of warm, moist air flowing in the opposite direction every time we exhale helps to restore them.

So much for the warming and moistening functions of the inner nose. But it is also there to act as a first line of defence, trapping dust, smoke, pollen, bacteria, viruses, fungi and any other potentially harmful foreign matter in the surrounding air. As Dr Lyall Watson points out in his fascinating book *Jacobson's Organ*, even in the least polluted areas of our planet, such as the middle of the South Pacific or Antarctica, every breath we take draws around 200,000 minute particles of debris into our lungs, while inhaling the polluted atmosphere around a six-lane highway in downtown Los Angeles during the rush hour can potentially flood your lungs with more than two million particles. These include an extraordinary mixture of natural and manufactured pollutants including:

'Salt, clay and ash from forest fires and distant volcanic eruptions. And mixed in with, or growing on, or simply being carried along by this fertile soil is a garden of exotic flora and fauna ... a few stray viruses in transit between their hosts; four or five common bacteria;

fifty or sixty fungi, including several rusts or moulds, one or two minute algae drifting in from the coasts; and possibly a fern or moss spore, or even an encysted protozoan.'

Little wonder, then, that nature should have equipped us with an extremely powerful and normally highly effective way for cleaning this potentially harmful gruel before it gets the chance to take up residence in our lungs. This involves a mucus-producing membrane that lines the inner nose and, like a fly paper capturing unwary bugs, traps the majority of airborne invaders. This can only happen efficiently of course, provided that the mucus remains moist — a crucial aspect of healthy breathing to which I shall return in a moment.

Fortunately, since all the muck adhering to our mucus membrane must be disposed of as rapidly as possible, nature has evolved an ingenious way of cleansing it. Millions of tiny cilia, hair-like structures, within the membrane, are constantly moving in a co-ordinated 'wafting' action that moves mucus and its contents into the throat, where they are swallowed and destroyed by the gut. Cilia move the mucus blanket so swiftly and efficiently that any microbes are unable either to make themselves at home or to make good their escape.

Maintaining Your Air-Conditioning Unit in Peak Condition

Since the nose is our first line of defence against potentially harmful invaders it is important, whenever possible, to take air in through your nostrils. Air entering through the mouth is drawn directly into the lungs through the pharynx and trachea without being filtered, moistened or warmed.

It is also essential to drink plenty of water (around 8 pints a day) to ensure your mucus remains moist. The drier it becomes the more vulnerable you are to airborne infections and pollution. At the same time, avoid too many starchy dishes or dairy products since these reduce the system's effectiveness by thickening the mucus and making it more viscous. Avoiding milk, cheese, butter, bread, pasta and so forth is especially important when suffering from colds, flu or any infection that already affects mucus production. Dry air in combination with already overly thickened mucus can cause a crusting within the nasal passages that results in discomfort, irritation and possibly inflammation.

Cleansing Your Passages with a Nasal Wash

To prevent a build up of muck and ensure their mucus membranes remain clean and healthy, more and more health conscious people are now using a nasal wash. This involves pouring a small amount of water into one nostril and allowing it to flow out of the other one.

To anybody who has accidentally sucked in water through their nose whilst swimming or bathing this may seem a highly undesirable thing to do. They know just how painful and disagreeable are the consequences of inhaling water. In fact there is a world of difference between a nasal wash, using water raised to a body temperature of 37 °C and with sufficient salt to give it the same composition as tears, and an inadvertent inhalation of chlorinated or chemically treated water.

Some people who regularly employ a nasal wash make use of a specially designed little container, called a Neti Pot, that is shaped rather like an Aladdin's lamp with a long, narrow spout. While this makes the procedure slightly easier, any small pot with a sufficiently narrow spout to direct the water accurately up your nostrils will prove satisfactory.

Try a nasal wash and you'll be delighted how much more clear-headed and energetic it makes you feel. When doing so follow these simple procedures carefully.

* Take a quarter of a teaspoon of fine salt – table salt is fine – and mix it with a cupful of warm water. There is no need to use a

thermometer to check the exact temperature so long as it feels about blood heat. Ensure the salt is completely dissolved before pouring half of it into your Neti Pot or other receptacle.

- With your head tilted to the right side and raised slightly, bend over the wash basin and gently pour the liquid into your left nostril. Adjust your position so that the fluid pours freely from your right nostril.
- When all the fluid has been used, blow through both nostrils to remove excess water and mucus. Never close a nostril whilst doing this or you may unintentionally force the fluid into the ear.
- Should you experience any problems in clearing your nasal passages, kneel down with your forehead touching the floor and, turning your head whilst doing so, blow air out through your nostrils.
- Now repeat the whole process with the remaining portion of the warm salted water, this time tilting your head to the left and pouring it in through your right nostril.
- With practice it becomes possible to direct the water downwards and out through the mouth which further cleanses the system.

From Nose to Lungs

From the nose, air passes down the windpipe or trachea, a tube some 15 mm wide and between 10 and 12 cm long. This divides into two bronchi and these into two bronchioles which, in turn, branch into smaller structures terminating in air sacks (alveoli) within the lungs.

At birth we possess around twenty-four million alveoli but by the time we are eight these have increased to the adult number of 300 million. If it were possible to flatten these out and place them side-by-side, they would cover an area approximately the dimensions of a tennis court.

The cone-shaped lungs are made up of relatively light and porous tissues that lie more or less freely in the thoracic cavity (chest), their apex immediately beneath the shoulders, their bases resting on the diaphragm and their surfaces making contact with the ribs and spine. A double layer of membrane known as pleura surrounds each lung. Between the two layers is a fluid that bathes the surfaces and prevents friction between the lungs and the chest wall during breathing.

The right lung has three lobes but the left lung only two, allowing a space for the heart which fits snugly between the two, lying mainly in a hollow in the inner left lung. Each lobe is composed of smaller divisions called lobules. A small bronchial tube enters each lobule and divides and subdivides, its walls becoming thinner and thinner before finally ending in the alveoli. Resembling tiny bubbles, these alveoli have walls just one cell thick which enable oxygen to pass through them and into the blood while carbon dioxide moves out of the blood and into the air. For this to happen efficiently there has to be a balance between the amount of blood flowing within the tiny vessels (capillaries) that surround the alveoli and the amount of oxygen within them. If the blood flow is insufficient the exchange of gases cannot take place successfully, even when there is plenty of oxygen available. It is a mismatch between the amount of air present in the alveoli and the amount of blood in the capillaries that causes most of the problems associated with lung diseases.

Because blood is influenced by gravity, our upright stance means that far more flows through the lower than the upper regions of the lungs, with the least amount being present at the top (apex). The differences are substantial. While around a litre of blood flows through the lower lobes of the lungs, in the upper regions closer to the collar bones this declines to around one tenth of a litre. Although the greater air flow in the upper part of the lungs partly reduces this mismatch, it is still important to breathe as deeply as possible to ensure air is drawn into the lower parts of the lung where the most blood is available to transport it. Unfortunately the majority of people fail to do so, using instead what I term 'upside-down breathing' whose negative effects I will be describing in the next chapter.

The Air We Breathe

The air we breathe comprises three main gases. The largest proportion (79 per cent) comprises the inert gas nitrogen, with oxygen making up 21 per cent and carbon dioxide just 0.03 per cent.

Once it has found its way into the capillaries, oxygen can be transported through the body by two basic mechanisms, either bound to the haemoglobin or dissolved directly into the blood plasma. Approximately 99 per cent of the oxygen transported in blood is bound chemically to haemoglobin, which is a protein contained within the red blood cells (erythrocytes). Each molecule of haemoglobin is capable of transporting four molecules of oxygen. The amount of oxygen that can be transported per unit volume of blood depends, therefore, on the concentration of haemoglobin. Normal haemoglobin concentration for a healthy male and female is approximately 150 g and 130 g, respectively, per litre of blood.

Haemoglobin can also carry carbon dioxide, a waste product from cells, which it picks up on the return trip to the heart and lungs. Oxygen and carbon dioxide should be the only molecules that bind to haemoglobin. However, other gases often present in our environment can also bind to red blood cells, so reducing or even preventing oxygen from attaching to haemoglobin. One gas that does so is carbon monoxide, present in high concentrations in both cigarette smoke and car exhaust fumes. Because this has an affinity for haemoglobin 240 times greater than oxygen, smokers may have between 5 and 15 per cent of all their haemoglobin taken up by this gas at any given time, even if they are not smoking at that particular moment. As a result they transport oxygen far less efficiently than do non-smokers.

Once haemoglobin becomes oxyhaemoglobin (oxygen–rich) it still has to travel throughout the body in order to supply the needs of individual cells, and the pumping force, which circulates the blood throughout the body, is, of course, the heart.

The right side of this pump takes in deoxygenated blood from the veins (carbon-dioxide-rich) and pumps it into the capillaries surrounding the alveoli in the lungs, where carbon dioxide passes out of the blood and oxygen is taken up by the red blood cells. This oxygen-rich blood is then redistributed to every cell in the body, its journey starting from the left side of the heart and passing via large arteries and then smaller and smaller blood vessels to all the 75 trillion cells making up our body.

When this oxygen-rich blood arrives at the cells it flows through increasingly tiny blood vessels to the point where the red blood cells must squeeze single file through capillaries. Here an exchange of gases similar to that within the lungs occurs. This time, however, the red blood cells drop off their molecules of oxygen and replace them with molecules of carbon dioxide (a by-product of cellular activity). This blood then returns to the heart through succession of increasingly large veins, eventually going through the right side of the heart and returning back to the lungs to complete the cycle.

The balance of these gases in the blood is extremely critical, as it is constantly being monitored by the brain and has a significant, and moment-by-moment, effect on the functioning of our nervous system. Increasing the rate at which you breathe by even a small amount, for instance, reduces the amount of carbon dioxide in the blood. This in turn raises the level of mental and physical arousal to such an extent that in some cases even such mild hyperventilation can trigger a full-blown panic attack. How and why this happens is something that I shall be discussing in the next chapter.

This whole intricate and delicately balanced process, on which life depends, requires not only that our heart and major blood vessels are all in good working order but also, of course, that sufficient fresh air is available within the lungs and that carbon dioxide is efficiently expelled by the lungs. Unfortunately this is by no means always the case. Indeed research suggests that fewer than a third of us breathes in such a way as to safeguard health and maximize mental and physical potential.

Your Health and the Breath You Take

A study of 153 heart patients in a coronary unit found that every single one of them breathed poorly, using the muscles of their chest rather than their diaphragm to take in and release a breath. Other studies have shown that breath therapy, either on its own or in conjunction with biofeedback and meditation, can have a beneficial effect in medical conditions including chronic pain, migraine headaches, high blood pressure (hypertension), asthma and panic attacks.

To the ancients this would come as no surprise; to us conditioned as we are to regard breathing purely in terms of an exchange of gases, the power of the breath often comes as a surprise. Yet there is not the slightest doubt that improving the way we breathe is the simplest, fastest and most effective way of enhancing well-being. Each breath we take and, especially, how we take it, exerts a powerful influence over everything from the health of our heart to the efficiency with which we digest dinner.

My research and clinical experience has also led me to conclude breathing plays an equally crucial role in the way we perform – especially when facing difficult or unfamiliar challenges. Indeed it can make the difference between success and failure, determining whether we achieve our true potential or are unable to accomplish those goals that should be well within our powers to attain.

In the next chapter we shall be taking a more detailed look at how and why problems arise when we explore the muscles by which we breathe and look at the two key ways of taking a breath – the usual way and the correct way!

CHAPTER SEVEN

The muscles by which we breathe

'Breathing the first pattern lays down the foundation for all the other succeeding patterns. Whenever the breathing is blocked in the body, future patterns will be blocked; whenever the breathing is free, the future patterns will develop efficiently.'
BONNIE BAINBRIDGE COHEN – SENSING, FEELING AND ACTION

While the nose, windpipe and other tubing allows air to pass into and out of the body, the bellows that cause the air to move in the first instance is provided by muscles in the upper body, especially those between the ribs (intercostals) and by the diaphragm.

Let's take a look at how these bones and muscles are arranged to provide the tireless and efficient mechanism on which our life depends.

Our roughly cylindrical torso consists of three separate regions:

* The thorax in which our lungs and heart are located.
* The abdomen lying directly beneath it and separated from it by the diaphragm, containing digestive organs.

- The pelvis, which extends from the hip bones to the bottom of the torso and contains organs responsible for reproduction and getting rid of waste.

The thirty-three vertebrae that make up the spine provide both the supporting structure and the framework around which the other tissues and organs are grouped. These vertebral bones are separated from one another by spongy shock absorbers known as vertebral discs.

Pairs of ribs are attached to the twelve vertebrae that support the thorax. Lying parallel to one another on each side of the chest, they curve forwards and downwards, with the first ten joined at the midline to the breastbone (sternum) to form a strong yet flexible cage. Because they increase in length and curvature from the top of the chest to the bottom the lower part of this ribcage is also the widest.

The Structure of our Breathing Bones

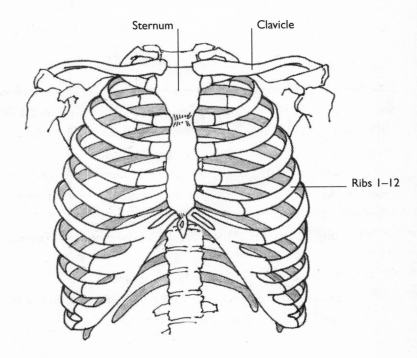

Sternum   Clavicle

Ribs 1–12

Attached to the lower ribs, the breastbone and spine is the diaphragm, separating chest and abdominal cavities. As we breathe in and out, the rise and fall of our chest and movement of the abdomen is produced by two sets of muscles known as the *primary* and *accessory* muscles of inhalation. Primary muscles are used only during quiet breathing at rest, while the accessory muscles come into action whenever we need to breathe more rapidly, such as during vigorous exercise. Accessory muscles may, however, be brought into use inappropriately as the result either of a physical problem, such a chronic obstructive lung disease, or a psychological one, such as a panic attack – which results in rapid, shallow breathing (hyperventilation).

During relaxed breathing the primary muscles contract in a co-ordinated fashion causing the diaphragm to move down and outwards as the ribs move upwards and out. This lowers the pressure inside the thorax causing air to flow into the lungs. These muscles then relax, allowing the breath to be expelled due to the elastic recoil of the lungs.

In theory there is nothing to prevent one inhaling so deeply and inflating the lungs to such an extent that the delicate alveoli burst under the pressure. In practice, however, this can never happen. Once the lungs have expanded to a critical point a reflex response inhibits inspiration and causes us to breathe out again. Conversely, deflating the lungs triggers another reflex that obliges us to take in a breath.

Our Primary Breathing Muscles

Three primary muscles are involved when we take a relaxed breath. The most important of these is the diaphragm, the others being the parasternal and scalenes.

Because the diaphragm is essential for deep, life-enhancing breathwork I shall describe its structure and function in more detail. As the illustration over the page shows, this large, yet thin, double-dome-shaped muscle fits inside our chest like a parachute, separating the lungs and the heart within the chest from the organs of digestion, such as the stomach, liver and intestines, within the abdomen.

The Organs Above and Below the Diaphragm

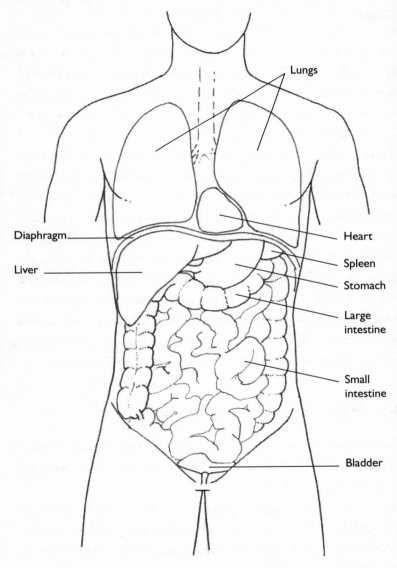

Lungs

Diaphragm

Heart

Liver

Spleen

Stomach

Large intestine

Small intestine

Bladder

At the top of the dome in the diaphragm is a central tendon, flattened somewhat to accommodate the heart that rests directly above it and is angled towards the left of the body. Radiating from this tendon are fibres that attach the diaphragm to the inner surfaces of the body. Frontally these fibres connect with the inner surface of a small structure at the end of your sternum known as the xiphoid process. At the sides they are attached to the seventh through to the twelfth ribs, and at the spine to the first through to the fourth lumbar vertebra.

When we breathe deeply and correctly the diaphragm contracts, forcing the guts downwards and forwards while simultaneously pulling the ribs upwards and outwards in what is sometimes described as a 'bucket-handle' motion. At the same time the parasternal muscles, which are attached to the breastbone and run between each rib, also contract, increasing the size of the chest cavity. The scalene muscles, lying on each side the neck, perform a similar action by raising the first and second rib while also helping to stabilize the chest wall. This creates a larger cavity inside the chest as a result of which the pressure inside the body falls below that of the surrounding atmosphere, causing air to flow into the lungs and restore the balance.

When the diaphragm relaxes and billows upwards inside the chest the air inside our lungs is compressed and flows out again during an exhalation. At the same time, as pressure within the chest falls, both the diaphragm and the parasternal muscles relax while the rib cage returns to its previous shape.

During quiet breathing this is a passive process requiring no muscular effort, made possible by the fact that our lungs and chest walls are elastic and, like a rubber band, tend to return to their starting position once the tension created during the inhalation is released. The process is, however, assisted by four abdominal muscles – the rectus abdominis, the external and internal obliques, and the transverses abdominis. All these muscles have attachments to the lower ribs so that contracting them decreases the size of the rib cage, so assisting in exhalation.

The first group of muscles form the so called 'six pack' that men who work out regularly like to flaunt on the beach. Unfortunately, as I shall explain in Chapter Eleven, when these frontal muscles are stronger than the others an imbalance is created that undermines what is termed 'core stability' and this inhibits healthy breathing.

In Part Two (Procedure One) you will be shown four simple, easily performed exercises that significantly enhance breathing by creating greater stability in this region.

Optimal Breathing vs. 'Normal' Breathing

During deep, health-enhancing breathing the diaphragm performs between 70 per cent and 80 per cent of all the work necessary, leaving the

Triangle Produced by Optimal Breathing Using the Primary Muscles

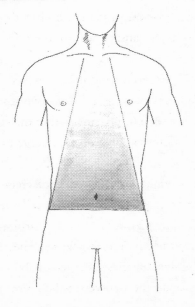

remainder to be done by the secondary respiratory muscles. When we breathe in this way a stable triangle is formed, as shown on the previous page. With its base extending across the centre of the body, this type of breathing creates a subjective feeling of being grounded and more in touch with our 'gut feelings'. Deep diaphragmatic breathing (DDB) which you will learn in Chapter Twelve will also help protect and nourish your spine.

Since, as we have seen, the diaphragm attaches along the front of the lumbar vertebrae, when it is able to move freely and easily this powerful muscle not only helps to stabilize the spine but also helps prevent bone degeneration and arthritic conditions by providing traction to the vertebral column. It also safeguards you against the agony of a trapped nerve while keeping the spongy intervertebral discs plump and healthy. Because, after the age of about twenty, these discs lack their own direct blood supply, their only way of remaining moist is by absorbing fluid from the surrounding tissues, something that only occurs during movement. In addition, regular rhythmic movement of the diaphragm gives all the organs of digestion, reproduction and excretion an excellent workout.

As Donna Farhi graphically puts it in *The Breathing Book*: 'When the diaphragm moves in the luxurious expansions that mark full breathing, all these organs are massaged, rolled, churned and bathed in new blood, fluids and oxygen … . Breathing stimulates all of the body to work better and this is why it has such a profound effect on our sense of well-being.' Without this massage the organs of digestion, the stomach, liver, spleen, intestines, colon and bladder, can become sluggish. Toxins are removed less efficiently and there is a reduction in the amounts of oxygen received by these organs.

Sadly for good health and maximum vitality this is not the way the majority of us breathe. Far more often the primary muscles do only 20 per cent of the work, with the secondary respiratory muscles – the scalenes, ternocleidomastoid, trapezius and pectorialis minor left to perform 80 per cent of the task. The result is to produce an unstable triangle (see below) whose apex faces downwards. This is known as 'upside-down' breathing.

Unstable Triangle Cause by Upside-Down Breathing Using the Secondary Muscles of Respiration

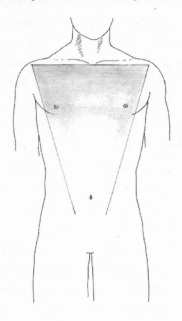

Upside-down breathing caused by neglecting the diaphragm as a primary muscle of breathwork is now almost universal in the developed world. This is not because we are born to breathe that way – indeed exactly the opposite is true – but because we have learned to breathe that way.

Watch a small baby at rest and you'll see that although her chest moves only slightly, her stomach rises and falls effortlessly with each inhalation and exhalation, clearly demonstrating her primary respiratory muscles are doing most of the work. She is breathing slowly, deeply and freely from her diaphragm. By the time this child reaches adolescence, however, the likelihood is that constant tension around her abdominal muscles will prevent them from expanding fully, so making it impossible for her diaphragm to flatten completely. These changes are a reflection both of the tensions imposed by growing up and of grown-up patterns of breathing copied from her parents. As Donna Farhi observes: ' Most breathing patterns are the accumulation of a lifetime's experience and they are as familiar to us as our way of walking. The nervous system has become conditioned to repeat these patterns even when the patterns are dysfunctional.'

'Upside-down' breathing adversely effects many aspects of health and performance – according to some medical researchers, it plays a role in around 75 per cent of illness. Fortunately, simply by changing the way you breathe, these problems can quickly and easily be rectified.

The Control of Your Breathing

As I have already explained, breathing provides us with a bridge between the conscious and unconscious mind since it is a function that can operate both entirely unconsciously and automatically and also under direct, conscious control. When functioning automatically, it is regulated by a so-called respiratory centre located within a part of the reptilian brain known as the medulla oblongata. This lies directly beneath the limbic system and so is both influenced reaching it from this region as well as influencing it in turn.

To understand these important interactions we must examine the way our nervous system functions. We have in fact not one but two distinct nervous systems known as the central nervous system (CNS) and the peripheral nervous system (PNS). The PNS can be further divided into one part that is responsible for controlling our skeletal muscles, such as our arms and legs, and a second that regulates organs like our gut, heart and glands. This second part, called the autonomic nervous system (ANS), takes care of essential but routine functions such as breathing and digesting food. The ANS is divided into two branches known as the sympathetic and the parasympathetic systems. The former speeds things up, for example by causing our heart to beat faster so that the blood can be pumped more rapidly. The latter slows things down again, restoring the body to normal running.

If you are frightened or angry the ANS triggers the fight or flight response that has evolved to help us survive in situations of objective danger. Among other changes it causes us to breathe more rapidly and this, as I have already explained, leads to chemical changes in the blood. These feed back into the system causing us to feel even angrier or more scared. By forcing ourselves to slow and deepen our breathing we feel calmer again. This is why learning to control breathing is so important to healthy living. It is the essential first step towards learning to regulate the autonomic nervous system, and by doing so, to bring under control such powerful emotions as fear, anxiety and anger. More than that, learning the different types of breathwork taught in Part Two of this book will allow you to exert greater control over the electrical patterns produced in your brain — literally over your own brain waves. What these waves are, how they arise and the ways in which they influence our thoughts and feelings will be described in the next chapter. By learning to control brain waves it becomes far easier to eliminate b–locks that are holding you back in life and preventing you from becoming the person you want to be.

Summary of Chapters Six and Seven

* The vast majority of the millions of breaths we take during our lives occur without conscious awareness.
* To Eastern sages, breathing held far greater significance than the mere exchange of gases. In Sanskrit breath is *prana*, signifying the vital energy of the universe.

- Your nose acts as an air-conditioning plant treating between 5 and 6 litres of air per minute, by purifying, warming and moistening it *en route* to the lungs.

- The nose is the body's first line of defence against potentially harmful invaders, so try always to breathe through this rather than through your mouth.

- Drinking 8 pints of water a day keeps the nasal mucus moist and safeguards you against infections and pollution.

- Avoid eating too many starchy dishes or dairy products since by thickening the mucus these foodstuffs make it less effective.

- Do not drink milk or eat cheese, butter, bread or pasta if suffering from colds, flu or any infection that already affects mucus production.

- The most powerful of our primary breathing muscles is the diaphragm, a thin, dome-shaped muscle attached to the lower ribs and breastbone at the front and the spine at the rear. During stable, optimal breathing this muscle performs around 80 per cent of the work involved.

- This type of breathing not only ensures that all the cells within our body receive adequate supplies of oxygen, it also helps ensure a healthy spine and internal organs.

- Unstable 'upside-down' breathing occurs when the secondary respiratory muscles do most of the work. This inefficient way of breathing is not natural but learned as we grow up. It reduces the amount of available oxygen and fails to massage the organs within our abdomen.

- Learning to control your breathing means you will not only regulate your emotional responses but also remove b-locks more rapidly and effectively by being able to produce specific patterns of brain waves on demand.

CHAPTER EIGHT

Your breathing and your brain waves

'Learning to control brain-wave patterns ... does not depend
on normal sensory feedback, but on the development of
awareness of subtle, internal sensations that normally we do
not notice ... through the use of this increased awareness we
train our bodies to function more optimally.'
ELMER AND ALYCE GREEN —BEYOND BIOFEEDBACK

On a sunny July morning in 1892 a young German cavalry officer
named Hans Berger was exercising his new mount when the horse
stumbled at the top of a steep embankment. The 19-year-old National
Service conscript fell heavily, rolling down the embankment and directly
beneath the thundering hoofs and flashing wheels of a galloping four-
horse gun battery. Miraculously when the battery had passed he
emerged shaken but unhurt by his hairbreadth brush with death.

That evening he received a telegram from his father asking after his
health. Berger senior explained that, at what turned out to be the precise
moment of the young man's near fatal accident, his sister had experienced
such a powerful premonition of danger for him, she insisted her father
telegraph to make sure he was safe. 'This (was) a case of spontaneous
telepathy ... at a time of mortal danger,' Berger recalled some twenty

years later. 'As I contemplated certain death, I transmitted my thoughts, while my sister, who was particularly close to me, acted as the receiver.'

Before the incident he had been intending to study astronomy, but impressed by his sister's apparent telepathic powers and eager to discover more about the workings of the brain he changed to neurology. Once qualified he began studying electrical activity within the head. Although these had first been detected in animals during the eighteenth century, it took more than two centuries for recording equipment to become sufficiently sensitive to measure the minute currents within the brain itself. In 1924, after years of research, Berger made the first ever recordings of brain waves through the skull of his 15-year-old son Klaus.

To accomplish this required overcoming enormous technical difficulties. Not only was his measuring equipment crude by modern standards, but he was trying to detect and record potentials of a few millionths of a volt through the bones of the skull and the far more powerful signals generated by muscles. He named these waves, with a frequency of between 8 and 14 cycles per second, Alpha waves, since they were the first to be detected.

By the time his life came to a tragic end in 1941, after the Nazis hounded him to suicide, Hans Berger's discoveries had established him as one of the key figures in brain research. The rhythmic patterns he first recorded are still sometimes referred to as Berger waves.

During the mid-fifties a British researcher, W. Grey Walter of the Burden Neurological Institute, developed what he called a 'toposcope'. This was capable of providing an instantaneous display of overall brain function on twenty-two cathode-ray tubes placed in an elliptical array to represent the shape of a patient's head as seen from above. This technical advance enabled neurologists to plot the timing of electrical waves in different parts of the brain. 'We now know that within the brain a great many electric processes can be identified, each with its own limited domain, some apparently independent, others interacting with one another,' commented Grey Walter. 'We must accept that in the EEG we are dealing essentially with a symphonic orchestral composition, but one in which the performers may move about a little, and may follow the conductor or indulge in improvisation – more like a jazz combination than a solemn philharmonic assembly. Only rarely can we sit in on this session – in ordinary EEG recording we hear only the rhythm section and an occasional break from far off.'

For many years the EEG was used primarily for diagnosing such medical conditions as tumours or epilepsy. In 1958, however, American psychologist Joe Kamiya pioneered an exciting new area of study in which he trained individuals to produce various brain patterns of electrical activity in their brain purely by thinking in a particular way. While conducting research into sleep, at the University of Chicago, Kamiya had become fascinated by the Alpha rhythm that could be seen appearing and disappearing in the EEGs of waking subjects. This caused him to wonder whether individuals could learn to become aware of and then produce at will this brain state.

To test the possibility he wired volunteers to an EEG and placed them alone in a darkened room. The electrical patterns produced by their brains were transmitted to a nearby laboratory where Joe Kamiya monitored and recorded them. From time to time he rang a bell in the next room and asked his subjects to guess whether or not they were producing Alpha waves. He then told them whether or not their guess was correct. On the first day his volunteers were right about half the time, a result one would expect from chance alone. By day two of the experiment, however, they were correct two-thirds of the time and by day three their success rate had soared to eight guesses out of ten, a result significantly better than could have been attained through chance alone. After only four days' training every subject was able to identify his or her own Alpha state with complete accuracy in 400 separate trials. Not only that but they could 'turn on' the Alpha state whenever they felt like it. Kamiya's research had clearly demonstrated that individuals were: 'able to control their minds to the extent of entering and sustaining either state upon command.'

As more and more people trained themselves to produce Alpha, important findings emerged about those who showed themselves to be especially adept at the task. They were, Kamiya reported, very agreeable people to work with 'I generally tend to have more positive liking for the individual who subsequently turns out to learn Alpha control more readily.'

Alpha is not, of course, the only electrical pattern produced by the brain. As the table below shows, several distinct types of frequency have been identified ranging from the long slow Delta waves that predominate in sleep to the fast Beta waves seen during intellectually demanding activities. The names given to these different 'brain waves' are based on their frequencies measured in Hertz (abbreviated to Hz) or cycles per second.

BRAIN WAVES

Name	Frequency (Hz)	State of Mind
Delta	0.5–3.0	Deep sleep.
Theta	4.0–7.0	Twilight sleep, the state between waking and sleeping. Also during moments of insight or when recalling some vivid memory.
Alpha	8.0–14	State of relaxed alertness. Brain not engaged on any specific activity. Receptive.
Beta	15–22	Alert, focused on mentally demanding task. Anxious or apprehensive.
High Beta	23–35	Brain highly active. Concentrating on complex problem or when anxious.
K-complex	35 +	Complex problem-solving. Consolidation of short-term memories. Occurs in brief bursts.

(Ranges are approximate and vary between individuals owing to the location of waves in different areas of the brain and differing response rates.)

How Brain Waves Develop

Studies of children aged from three months to nineteen years, conducted by Charles E. Henry of Western Reserve University School of Medicine, have shown how these different frequencies change during our development from infancy to adulthood.

Between three and four months the frequencies observed most often are slow Delta waves, reflecting the infant's long periods of sleep. By a year old these have given ground to Theta waves which continue to dominate until around the age of five. From then on Alpha waves begin to appear until, by the time a youngster has reached his or her teens, they are equal to Theta. As children grow into their teens, however, Theta slowly declines while Alpha increases and Beta begins to make an appearance. Adults, without special training to recapture the relaxed alertness that characterizes the mental states of most young children, typically produce far more Beta than Alpha waves.

So what do each of these states of mind represent in terms of how we think, feel and behave?

Subjective Mental State Associated with Alpha Waves

The description most often given is one of relaxed alertness. You feel calm and tranquil while still being aware of events around you. Those who have learned meditation, yoga or a similar 'mind centring' discipline, as well as people with healing powers, typically produce the strongest Alpha and are usually able to do so with the least effort.

Alpha waves increase significantly when we close our eyes, an effect that led some sceptics incorrectly to suggest they were nothing more than an artefact produced by electrical impulses from the muscles around the eye. However, careful studies have confirmed that they are genuine and important aspects of brain function.

Alpha waves are also associated with many pleasurable and rewarding social or leisure activities. During the sixties, electrical activity in the brains of American footballers was monitored while they were playing in actual matches, and high levels of Alpha were consistently recorded immediately after a successful touchdown.

Maxwell Cade, an eminent British researcher, identified what he termed a 'dowsing' Alpha, short bursts of low voltage waves that appear some half a second before the dowsing reaction occurs. 'When asked to stand still with eyes closed the dowser showed the usual high level of Alpha from both hemispheres,' Cade reported. 'As he began to walk with eyes closed over the same ground, this steady Alpha was replaced by Alpha bursts, such that it was impossible to say from the EEG whether his eyes were open or closed. Presumably as soon as the dowser gave his attention to walking, the Alpha from the occipital lobe (visual centre of the brain) "blocked" whereas the dowsing Alpha appears from a different area of the brain.'

Subjective Mental State Associated with Beta Waves

Measure electrical activity in the brain of someone solving a tricky problem or making a difficult decision and you are likely to find a predominance of Beta waves with a range of between 14 Hz and 26 Hz. These waves, which more closely resemble flurries of static than the smooth rhythms associated with Alpha, are present during active thinking, paying close attention to something in the outside world and when solving complex problems. However the relationship between mental and electrical activity is less straightforward than this suggests. When asked to carry out a simple calculation, such as 143 minus 67, for example, most people show increased Beta production. Yet if requested to find the square roots of numbers, in their head, the same individuals tend to produce more Alpha waves. A possible explanation is that while we all know how to perform simple subtraction most of us have forgotten how to find a square root. As a result we have to dredge up memories of school maths classes to recall the necessary procedure. Since this involves delving into the memory banks of the limbic system, the high regions of thought (the neo-cortex) remain relatively inactive allowing Alpha to predominate.

A professional mathematician, well practised at finding square roots, might therefore be assumed to produce less Alpha and more Beta. Yet, intriguingly, some of the world's greatest intellects, such as Albert Einstein, have been found to continue producing mainly Alpha waves even when solving complex problems. Only around one person in ten of the normal population produces almost continuous Beta and very little Alpha. This is possibly as a result of high anxiety levels – Beta waves increase significantly when we are fearful – but could also be due to their possessing a more than usually alert and active brain.

Subjective Mental State Associated with Theta Waves

Theta waves, with a frequency of between approximately 5 and 7 cycles per second, appear approximately half way between the back and the front of the brain in what are known as the temporal and parietal regions. They are usually strongest on the left side. Theta waves appear to be associated with emotional states, since children generate a large quantity when laughing or crying.

In adults the ending of a pleasant activity also increases Theta output. As with Alpha, our brain produces higher levels of Theta when we close our eyes, and it appears most strongly as consciousness slips towards drowsiness. During this half-way house between waking and sleeping, a mental state the English poet and psychical researcher Frederick Myers termed hypnagogic sleep (from the Greek *hypnos*, 'sleep' plus *agogos*, 'leading') the mind is typically full of vivid and often bizarre images.

Myers used the term 'hypnapopmic images' to describe the very vivid dreams that occur as we are drowsily awakening. Unlike daydreams these startling images appear to be a projection of impulses from below the levels of normal awareness, that is from our limbic system.

Lucid dreams, in which we are aware of dreaming and are able to control, at least to some extent, the action of those dreams, are most likely to arise during these Theta–dominated brain states. While in Theta many people become highly creative and able to use their imaginations to make associations that might never come to them in a more alert state. So powerful are these creative impulses that many whose livelihood depends on coming up with highly original ideas strive to find ways of holding themselves on the tightrope between waking and sleeping.

The prolific American inventor Thomas Edison, for example, would sit in a comfortable chair while holding a metal ball in his outstretched right hand directly above a steel plate. He would then drift off into a hypnagogic reverie on the very edge of sleep while he contemplated his next designs. If he toppled over into sleep his hand relaxed, the ball fell and the noise awakened him. In this way he was able, with some practice, to maintain high levels of Theta while remaining awake. As you will discover in Chapter Fifteen the same result can be achieved entirely by learning to breathe in a specific way.

Subjective Mental State Associated with Delta Waves

Delta waves, the slowest waves of all with frequencies as low as 0.5 Hz are found mainly during sleep. Neurologist Grey Walter, emphasizing their protective function, compared them to the 'dead man's handle' on a railway train: 'During Delta activity no useful work can be done by the neurones concerned,' he commented. 'Sometimes the Delta waves are so large that we may suspect them of paralysing the cortex by electrocution, as it were, and we may speculate as to whether this may not be their special function in certain conditions, just as the function of pain is sometimes to immobilize an injured part.'

By preventing the muscles from obeying commands from the sleeping brain, animals and humans avoid harming either themselves or others.

Normal Brain Waves Contain All Types of Frequencies

In a healthy adult you find a mix of different wavelengths that vary according to whatever activity that individual is engaged on, from higher levels of Theta and Alpha associated with relaxed alertness to a pattern dominated by Beta during intellectually demanding or anxiety-arousing challenges. Not only does this pattern vary overall, it also varies between the two hemispheres of the brain. The bar chart below illustrates the pattern of activity present in a 32-year-old male as he was engaged in a routine but not disagreeable task.

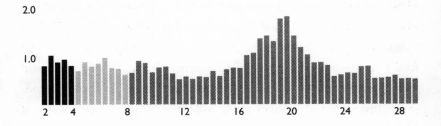

Brain action during an alert mental state with low Theta and Alpha waves (4-14 Hz) and high Beta waves (from 15 Hz upward)

Along the base of the bar chart we find the frequencies of each of the wave bands, from Delta at the extreme left to Beta at the right. The height of each bar indicates the strength of each frequency in the spectrum. Here a 2-minute reading has been sampled, and averaged, over a 30-second period.

In Appendix One you will find similar graphs showing the target pattern of brain waves developed during each of the breakthrough breathwork procedures taught in Part Two.

The Eighties Alpha Fad

Joe Kamiya's work launched a flood of popular and commercial interest in Alpha training, with many outlandish and ridiculous claims being made in order to promote the sales of gadgets that claimed to provide 'instant Zen' by producing Alpha at the press of a button. Not that all these devices were the electronic equivalent of snake oil – some were well designed and did what they claimed to do, at least so far as increasing Alpha production was concerned. Unfortunately the hype reached extraordinary levels – at the peak of interest you could even check into special Alpha 'bars' and order a 'high' just as one might order a Martini.

In 1986 when my book on the subject, *The Alpha Plan,* appeared there was still such interest in the topic that the BBC produced a documentary entirely about my research in this field. A few years later, however, the fad had passed. While many researchers, myself included, continued with these studies and those with an interest in expanding their potential took up biofeedback Alpha training, popular interest was well and truly over. It had been destroyed to a large extent not because all the claims made for Alpha states were false, but because they had been hyped far beyond what was technically and biologically possible.

So why am I revisiting the Alpha studies now – and what has this got to do with breathing? Simply this. To break through emotional barriers to our progress through life, to overcome many stress- and anxiety-related problems and achieve all we are capable of achieving, requires what may be described as a 'reprogramming' of our limbic system, that region of our brain that is unresponsive to logical analysis and reassuring words.

Studies conducted by my colleagues and myself have shown that removing b-locks that prevent us achieving our full potential can best be accomplished when the brain is generating a specific pattern of electrical activity. This normally includes a high proportion of Alpha (8–14 Hz), some of the higher Theta (4–8 Hz) bands as well as lower level Beta (14 Hz–24 Hz). The exact proportion of each of these frequencies within the overall mix varies according to the type of activity involved and the nature of the b-lock to be removed. Each of these required states can be generated at will by adopting the pattern of breathing described in the appropriate training programme.

Having established the desired pattern of brain waves, the next step is to bring about the desired changes in behaviour. These range from combating stress and anxiety to eliminating emotional b-locks arising within the limbic system. The way in which this can be achieved is through the procedure I call sensualization, and in the next chapter I shall explain what this involves and how to make it work for you.

Summary of Chapter Eight

- The brain produces electrical patterns that can be measured using an EEG (electroencephalogram).
- These range from long slow Delta waves present during sleep to high-frequency (14 Hz and upwards) Beta waves most often found when the brain is either engaged in an intellectually demanding task or when we are feeling apprehensive or agitated.
- The first pattern to be recorded was of Alpha waves (8 Hz–14 Hz) which tend to dominate the brain waves of people who

meditate or follow a similar mental discipline. Subjectively they are associated with feelings of relaxed alertness.

- Theta waves (4 Hz–8 Hz) predominate when we are drowsily waking up or falling asleep. Subjectively they are associated with high levels of creativity.

- The development of these waves occurs throughout childhood, but by our late teens the adult spectrum has been established. A typical adult waking EEG, therefore, contains a wide range of frequencies from long slow Delta waves through to fast-moving Beta waves.

- My studies have shown that the removal of b-locks and the enhancement of all types of performance is most easily achieved when the mind is producing specific patterns of electrical activity or 'brain waves'.

CHAPTER NINE

The power of sensualization

'The sorcery and charm of imagination and the power it gives the individual to transform his world into a new world of order and delight, makes it one of the most treasured of all human capacities.'
FRANK BARRON: *A SOURCE BOOK FOR CREATIVE THINKING*

Greek orators had a major problem. With their speeches lasting for several hours, and without the benefit of either cue cards or autocues to provide a prompt, they were obliged to develop powerful and practical ways of remembering and recalling vast amounts of information. Not surprisingly this led some entrepreneurs to develop and market a number of mnemonic devices for aiding a flagging memory. Named after Mnemosyne, the personification of memory in Greek mythology, they create in the mind an artificial structure that allows disassociated ideas to brought to mind more easily. Perhaps the best known of these are phrases such as: 'Richard of York Gave Battle in Vain' (for the colours of the rainbow – Red, Orange, Yellow, Green, Blue, Indigo and Violet) or 'Most Volcanoes Erupt Mulberry Jam Sandwiches Under Normal Pressure' (for the planets outward from the sun – Mercury, Venus, Earth, Mars, Jupiter, Saturn, Uranus, Neptune and Pluto). One that has remained firmly fixed in my own mind some twenty years after studying neurophysiology is 'On Old Olympus Towering Top a Finn and German Vault and Hop' which aids recall of the twelve cranial nerves in order of precedence.

However, clever as such memory tricks are – and they all carry with them the danger that you will recall the mnemonic perfectly but forget what the letters actually stand for – they clearly fall far short of what is needed to learn a lengthy oration. What is needed here is something both more complex and subtler.

First off the mark with such a system was a fifth century BC Greek lyric poet named Simonides of Ceos. He developed a mnemonic technique known as *loci et res*, from *locus* meaning a familiar structure and *res* the thing to be remembered. It was a simple yet powerful device that allowed the lengthiest of speeches to be remembered with relative ease. How he came to devise this approach is an intriguing story that well illustrates some of the key aspects of sensualization.

Simonides – The World's First Commercial Memory Man

While attending a banquet in a luxurious marble hall, Simonides was unexpectedly called outside to meet two messengers. No sooner had he left the building than an earthquake caused its collapse and everyone remaining inside was killed. So crushed were their bodies by the gigantic falling pillars that even their next of kin were unable to recognize them.

In despair they begged the sole survivor of the catastrophe to help identify their loved ones. So many of his friends and neighbours had attended the banquet that, at first, Simoniades felt unable to help. He simply could not remember where each of his friends had been sitting. Then he realized that by recreating an image of the banqueting hall in his mind's eye he could place each of the guests in his seat and so recall their names. Sitting quietly he focused on picturing the banqueting hall at the moment he was called away. 'Walking' through this imaginary chamber he was able accurately to name each of the victims so that grieving relatives could remove the crushed remains of their loved ones. Later it struck him that this same approach could prove of great value to orators – and so one of the world's first ever memory enhancement course was created.

Even today, more than 2,500 years after the event, the 'method of loci' remains a staple technique in many of the memory training courses you see advertised in newspapers and magazines.

The Method of Loci

Simonides instructed his students to imagine themselves strolling around a familiar building, such as their own homes, mentally locating each key idea or fact in a specific location. One, for example, might be mentally fixed just inside the front entrance, the second on a table, a third by an ornamental fountain in the courtyard and so on. To recall those ideas or facts the speaker had merely to retrace his footsteps around the same location – in his mind's eye of course – and as it were 'pick up' the information where he had previously positioned it.

The same approach works just as well today. To remember a shopping list, for example, try visualizing each item at a specific place in your own home. You might put a bag of sugar on the hall table, a half kilo of apples on the TV in the drawing room and potatoes on the dining room table. To recall the list simply retrace your steps around the house.

The power of visualization as a memory aid is well illustrated by the experiment below. Try it and you'll be amazed at just how effective it can be.

Testing the Power of Images

Start by reading through the twenty nouns below once only. Now close the book and write down as many as you can recall and, if possible, in the order they appeared.

Aeroplane, Pumpkin, Kitten, Dunce's Cap, Harmonium, Jelly, Forest, Castle, Chariot, Rocking Chair, Shotgun, Banquet, Bread, Stone, Cream, Ship, Snowmen, Television, Oak Tree, Catapult.

How did you get on? Most likely you found it easiest to recall the words at the beginning and end of the list. This is known as the primacy and recency effect, since we recall most accurately what we hear first and what we hear last, but become confused about what goes on around the middle. This is why public speakers are often advised to 'tell the audience what you intend to tell them, tell them, and finally tell them what you told them' in order that the primacy and recency effects will ensure maximum recall.

Although it may seem like a task suitable only for a person with a so-called 'photographic memory' it is perfectly possible to remember and accurately recall that list – or even one twice as long – in just one reading. Not only that but you can just as easily repeat every word from finish to start or begin anywhere you like and move either backwards or forwards through the list. Prove this for yourself right now by using a slight modification of Simonides idea.

Instead of placing each word at a different location around your home (although this would work just as well it is a slightly harder approach to master) you construct a 'mind movie' in which each item on the list is recalled as a vivid and bizarre image. The more unusual you make your 'movie' the easier and more accurate recall will be.

Turning That List into a Crazy Mind Movie

Visualize an aeroplane made from a giant pumpkin. Try and vividly picture a bright orange pumpkin fitted with wings, jet engines and a tail hurtling through the sky above. Now see the pumpkin/plane being flown by a fluffy black-and-white kitten, with her paws on the control column. Because she is not a very good pilot, the kitten is wearing a dunce's cap, a white cone on which a big 'D' is written in bright red ink. At the same time as trying to fly the aircraft the kitten is playing an old fashioned harmonium made from jelly. Notice how this jelly harmonium wobbles as it is played ... Proceed in the same way for the entire list and, when you reach the final word 'catapults', imagine them firing something into the sky and attempting to hit an aeroplane made from a giant pumpkin.

By doing this you will have transformed a list into a continuous loop, so making it easier to start or end at any word. Try this for yourself and you will be astonished at how good your memory – which perhaps in the past you tended to denigrate – really is.

Visualizations and Sporting Success

The importance of visualization as an aid to enhancing athletic performance is now so widely recognized that very few élite sportsmen or women would dream of competing without first mentally rehearsing every aspect of their upcoming challenge.

'It's been called "going to the movies",' says Ray Floyd, winner of the PGA, Master's and US Open. 'It may be the most important part of your mental package.'

Swimmer Alex Bauman, double Olympic Gold Medallist, has no doubt about the vital role 'mind movies' have played in his own considerable sporting success: 'My visualization has been refined more and more as the years go on. That is what really got me the world record and Olympic medals.'

Golfing ace Jack Nicklaus says that prior to playing he spends time visualizing his ball landing on the green and watching it bounce. Next he visualizes the arc of the ball in flight, his swing, and finally the ball leaving the ground. He joins these images together in the correct sequence — his swing, the ball's trajectory, its landing and bouncing on the green — in order to achieve the perfect stroke.

Here's how triathlete Sally Edwards describes her preparations for the 1991 Ironman-Hawaii Triathlon in which she was racing to win in the master's (40-44 years) age division: 'As always I set my race plan and visualized it in advance. On race day I replayed that mental video. I knew just about when the monkey of fatigue was going to jump on my back during the 112-mile bike ride leg.' There were many occasions during the eleven hours of fierce competition that she suffered pangs of self-doubt. On each occasion, by switching on her 'mind movie', Sally was able to confirm that this particular setback had been allowed for in her overall visualization which, she is convinced, led her to final victory.

The competitive edge that visualization can give to sportsmen and women, no matter what sport they play, is demonstrated by the fact that one tennis player who had been beaten in 85 per cent of her games prior to visual imagery training lost only one during the remainder of the season.

In cricket a bowler raised his average from 185 before training to 215 afterwards, while in basketball one player improved from shooting 61 per cent from the free-throw line and 38 per cent from the floor to 90 per cent and 50 per cent respectively.

Mental rehearsal has also been shown to have a positive effect on motivation. In one study of novice golfers, for instance, it was found that not only did those using imagery spend more time practising and stick more closely to their training schedules, they also set higher goals and had more realistic expectations. The effects of this type of mental rehearsal are not only of benefit to athletes, however. As we shall see, everyone can make use of them both to improve their performance and to ensure they remain within their O–Zone throughout the challenge. Not that the effects of visualisation are 'all in the mind'.

Visualizations Affect both Mind and Body

As long ago as the 1930s psychologist Edmund Jacobson demonstrated that if you visualize yourself performing some action, such as lifting a weight with your right arm, the muscles in that arm show increased electrical activity. Other researchers have found that picturing something travelling across your field of vision, such as a running animal, results in more eye muscle activity than imagining the same animal stationary.

At the University of Lowell in Massachusetts, cognitive psychologist Robert Kunzendorf measured electrical patterns produced in the retinas of twenty volunteers, five of whom were capable of producing extremely vivid mental imagery. First he asked each to look at different coloured lights being flashed before them and found that, for example, red produced one pattern, green another and yellow a third. When he next asked the five skilled visualizers merely to imagine those same lights flashing he found exactly the same electrical patterns were produced. More remarkably still, when he flashed one colour – say red – onto the screen, but told them to imagine it was another colour – for instance green – they regularly reported seeing that other colour. What's more, in a quarter of the cases their eyes responded as if they were actually seeing that different colour!

Visualizations in Clinical Practice

The power of the imagination to help heal the body is well documented. One of the first medical practitioners to exploit visualizations for the benefit of his cancer patients was Dallas radiation oncologist O. Carl Simonton. He used a combination of relaxation and vivid mind movies, in which terminally ill cancer patients pictured themselves attacking the tumour, for instance by imagining their white blood cells as white knights triumphing over the dark forces represented by cancerous cells. In many cases the tumours reduced in size and in some there was a complete remission of the disease.

Other studies have shown that appropriate imagery can strengthen our immune system and play a beneficial role in overcoming a wide range of health difficulties, including asthma, depression, anxiety and sexual dysfunction.

But bear in mind that the power of the imagination can be used to harm as well as enhance physical performance. Negative, gloom-filled images of failure will undermine your chances of success just as surely as positive mental imagery can improve it. Indeed, on occasions such images can, literally, prove lethal.

One of the most dramatic instances of negative imagery's fatal power occurred when Nick, a young railway yardman known to have a vivid but pessimistic imagination, was accidentally locked inside an isolated refrigerated boxcar in the freight yard. The other workers had left early to celebrate the foreman's birthday and no one was around to witness the accident or hear his ever more desperate cries for help.

Finally Nick slumped on the floor in despair. While there was plenty of fresh air in the car, he could already feel the cold seeping into his bones. Into his mind came vivid images of his body getting colder and colder. He began to tremble violently as the zero temperature started to gnaw at his bones, seeing ice form around his blue lips and on his eye-lids. Feeling himself becoming weaker and weaker to the point of death, one of his last acts was to find a piece of cardboard and scrawl a final poignant message to his wife and family. 'So cold, body's getting numb,' he wrote piteously. 'If I could just go to sleep. These may be my last words.'

The next morning when help arrived it was too late. The fit young man was lying dead on the boxcar floor, his final message beside him. An autopsy showed every physical sign that he had frozen to death. But the remarkable thing about the tragic accident was this. Because the refrigeration unit on the boxcar was faulty the temperature inside had never fallen below 61°F. The young man had imagined himself to death!

Demonstrate for yourself the way in which visualization can affect the body by means of the following simple experiment.

Turning Your Fingers into a Ring of Steel

For this you will need the assistance of someone whose physical strength more or less approximates your own. Here's what you do.

Form a circle using your thumb and first finger of your right hand. Now ask a friend to try and break the circle apart using a finger from each of their hands.

The chances are that, unless that person is much weaker than you are, they'll have little or no difficulty in doing so.

Now imagine a steel ring inside the circle formed by your finger and thumb. Not only should you attempt to see this as vividly as possible, for instance by picturing the light glinting off the shiny surface of the steel, but also to feel it pressing against your skin. Notice the cold hard strength of the metal and the pressure your muscles are exerting on it. Once again invite your friend to try and break the circle by pulling your fingers apart. On this occasion, unless they are significantly stronger than you, the challenge is likely to prove beyond them.

The Importance of Visual Rehearsal

Your imagination can also be used to create a unique training ground in which to rehearse any new behaviours that might be difficult or embarrassing in real life.

The advantage of exploiting the unlimited freedom the theatre of your mind provides is that it becomes easily possible to develop as many different versions of any situation as you wish. By doing so, you can then to compare likely outcomes to the various approaches you might decide to take and the different responses you might want to make – and all within the privacy of your mind. Imagining yourself carrying out some activity as you would ideally wish to do it makes it far easier to perform with the same degree of excellence in real life.

When sportsmen and women use visual rehearsal to improve on their personal best performance, for example, they may imagine themselves competing at a familiar course or athletics track, taking part in a highly competitive game or recovering from early setbacks and storming through to victory. Apart from enabling them, and you, to explore an almost unlimited number of possible scenarios, visual rehearsals have the additional benefit of ensuring more accurate recall of any problems or errors that occurred. While memory of the event can often be misleading, re-running an event in the mind's eye is likely to prove more precise.

A professional skier disqualified for falling during a race, for example, was convinced this tumble had been caused by a sudden change in snow conditions. By recreating that event in his mind's eye, he quickly realized his recollection of the incident had been at fault. The tumble was due not to any change in the snow but resulted from placing his weight on the wrong ski at the turn. Having recognized where the problem lay he then imagined himself overcoming it during a mental rehearsal in which he not only saw the event but also felt the wind on his face, the coldness of the air on his skin and the sounds as he hurtled down the slope. He also became aware of which muscles were appropriately or inappropriately tensed at different moments in the competition. By incorporating these additional sensations, such as the coldness of the air, the sounds of the race and how his weight was being distributed into this 'mind movie' he had transformed a visualization into a sensualization.

As I will explain in a moment, the more sensations – sounds, taste, touch and smell – you include the more powerful and effective the technique will prove. But, as I shall also point out, if the sensualization is to prove of maximum possible benefit, you first need to create a state of mind in which certain brain waves predominate. The only way to achieve this rapidly and reliably is by adopting the specific patterns of breathing described in Part Two.

Sensualizations in Practice

Sensualizations can be used to enhance your performance and remain within your O–Zone in any activity where you feel you are not currently achieving all you are capable of achieving, from making friends to making love; passing driving tests to coming over well in job or promotion interviews. You can use them to set and clarify your key goals, increase motivation, improve concentration, focus your energy and attention more accurately, boost self-confidence when confronting fresh challenges, reduce stress, improve your public speaking; cope with aggressive confrontations, improve physical and mental well-being and bring performance-zapping anxiety under control.

Your Limbic System Doesn't Speak English!

A further essential point to keep in mind is that, while our limbic system – which is of course where memories are laid down – cannot understand verbal commands, it is strongly influenced by more basic and primitive forms of communication, such as images, smells, sounds and bodily sensations. For this reason b–locks within the limbic system, as I described in the case histories, are far more rapidly and efficiently removed by using this approach than with any other method.

In her thought-provoking book *Drawing on the Right Side of the Brain* American psychologist and art teacher Betty Edwards asks why it is that the majority of adults seem to have a drawing ability rather worse than that of most 12-year-olds! The answer she proposes is not that adults lack either a child's hand-eye co-ordination or their mechanical dexterity. Rather, she claims, it is because while growing up we gradually lose our ability to 'see'. By this she means that visual perception changes from being a largely right brain process to one occurring more often in the logical left hemisphere of the brain. As a result the intuitive and creative experiences of childhood where the right hemisphere is in the ascendancy give way to rigorous analysis. This results in a sort of 'sighted blindness' in which we see without actually seeing and perceive without fully perceiving.

She also offers a simple but insightful way of demonstrating this effect for oneself. All you need to do is take a fairly complicated line drawing and copy it twice. The first time have the original the right way around but on the second occasion turn it upside-down. Unless you have a truly artistic streak, your second copy – made from the inverted drawing – should be a significant improvement on the first. Try it and see for yourself.

Why does this happen? Her explanation, which seems entirely reasonable, is that when the drawing is the right way up the left hemisphere takes command of the task and imposes a logic on the drawing that prevents you from actually seeing what is in front of your eyes. When, however, the picture is upside-down the left hemisphere abandons the attempt to make logical sense of it and surrenders control to the right side of the brain. Once the right hemisphere takes charge, you are able to see the image more clearly and so reproduce it more accurately.

Part of the value of sensualization training is not just that it will help you liberate yourself from performance restricting b-locks but that it will help you to sense every aspect of the world about you more clearly and vividly than you may have done for years. It will fine-tune all your sensations, enabling you to see more clearly, hear more acutely, smell, taste and touch your environment more vividly than you have done since early childhood. In this way even the most ordinary and mundane of surroundings may be transformed into richly rewarding sensory experiences.

Before starting to train yourself in creating vivid and powerful sensualizations it would be as well to establish just how good your current powers really are. This will provide you with a baseline from which to monitor your progress while developing this invaluable skill.

Testing Your Powers of Sensualization

To do this I'd like you to spend a few moments visualizing a ripe juicy lemon. Picture the fruit as vividly as you can in your mind's eye. If it helps then feel free to close your eyes. Imagine that you are holding the lemon in your left hand while studying the colour and texture very carefully. Notice the different shades of yellow and the stipple effect of the skin. Feel it resting in your hand and notice the cold firmness of the fruit against your skin. Now take hold of an imaginary kitchen knife in your right hand and slice the lemon in two. Feel the weight of the sharp blade in your hand as you raise it. Hear the swish as it cleaves through the air, the slight thud as it strikes the fruit and the plop as one of the severed section falls from your grasp. Notice how your fingers tightened to grasp the fruit and the knife. Imagine how the muscles in your upper arm must have moved first to raise the blade and then to bring it slicing down. See droplets of juice spurting out as you make the cut and smell the pungent citric aroma. Finally take one half of the imaginary lemon and raise it slowly to your lips. Anticipate then experience the sharp acid taste of the juice as, placing the slice between your lips, you slowly but deliberately suck it. If your sensualization was reasonably strong then you will notice an increase in saliva in response to the mental image.

Now score each of the sensations you sought to experience (sights, sounds, muscle movements, touch, taste and smell) on the six rating sheets below. I suggest that you do not permanently mark the book while doing so since you will want to return to these rating sheets time and again as you perfect your sensualization abilities.

Sensualization Rating Scales

1. Imagery

Sensation of Sight	Score
As clear and as vivid as in real life	5
Almost as clear and vivid as in real life	4
Reasonably clear and vivid	3
Not particularly clear or vivid	2
Only a fleeting impression	1
No image at all	0

2. Sounds

Sensation of Sounds	Score
As sharp and clear as in real life	5
Almost as sharp and clear as in real life	4
Reasonably sharp and clear	3
Not particularly sharp or clear	2
Only a fleeting impression	1
No sounds at all	0

3. Smell

Sensation of Smell	Score
As clear and as vivid as in real life	5
Almost as clear and vivid as in real life	4
Reasonably clear and vivid	3
Not particularly clear or vivid	2
Only a fleeting impression	1
No smell at all	0

4. Taste

Sensation of Taste	Score
As clear and as vivid as in real life	5
Almost as clear and vivid as in real life	4
Reasonably clear and vivid	3
Not particularly clear or vivid	2
Only a fleeting impression	1
No taste at all	0

5. Touch

Sensation of Touch	Score
As clear and as vivid as in real life	5
Almost as clear and vivid as in real life	4
Reasonably clear and vivid	3
Not particularly clear or vivid	2
Only a fleeting impression	1
No sense of touch at all	0

6. Kinaesthetic

Sensation of Muscle Movements	Score
As if I was moving my arm in real life	5
Almost as if it was really happening	4
Reasonably life-like	3
Only occasionally sensations of movement	2
Barely perceptible sensations of movement	1
No impression of movement at all	0

Now total your score on all six ratings and compare them with the results below:

20–30 points: Very few people can achieve the maximum possible score of 30 points without training but any score above 20 is good and indicates that you have already developed this natural talent to a high degree. You should therefore experience little or no difficulty when incorporating sensualization into the procedures described in Part Two.

12–19 points: Average score. You have an excellent basis of skills on which to build. During the training exercises that follow concentrate especially on those aspects of the sensualization where you found it especially hard to evoke the sensation desired.

11 or below: You are clearly having difficulty with some, if not all, of the various sensory elements that comprise a sensualization. But even if your score was on the low side do not feel discouraged. The following exercises will allow you to develop this talent, which we all possess and merely need to work at to perfect.

Exercises for Building Powerful Sensualizations

The six exercises below involve listening, smelling, touching, tasting and becoming aware of how your muscles are working to a far higher intensity than is usually the case. I suggest that you start by working with the sensations you found it hardest recreate in your imagination. If you found all of them equally difficult to sensualize start by improving your powers of visual imagery, as most people find this the easiest sensation to develop. Next start adding sounds to those sights, then include sensations of smell, touch and — where appropriate — taste, before working on muscle movements.

There is no need to set about creating formal training sessions, merely take whatever opportunities offer themselves to heighten all your senses by developing a greater awareness of your surroundings in a variety of different situations. At first just occupy yourself for a couple of minutes as you will probably find it hard to focus for much longer on the task without finding your concentration disrupted by intruding thoughts, ideas and concerns. With only a little practice, however, you will find it easier and easier to focus the mind on just one sensory input — such as sights or sounds — for longer and longer periods.

Exercise 1: Developing Your Visual Sense

When out and about during the normal working day start paying careful attention to all that you see while taking far less notice of information from your other senses. Start by reviewing the whole scene before you. Then start to focus in on smaller and smaller details.

When walking in the country, for example, survey the whole of a landscape as if seeing everything before you eyes for the first time in your life. Notice the way fields intersect, how hedges, walls or fences follow the contours of the landscape. Observe the shadows cast by trees and hedgerows; become aware of different colours, tones, shades and hues. After a while transfer your gaze to examine more minutely some detail in your surroundings, such as the texture of bark, the way sunlight spills through leaves, droplets of dew on the grasses or the fine tracery of a spider's web.

If in a town or city study the shape of buildings, the slant of roofs and the textures of walls.

Examine shop window displays observing the design, shape and colours of items displayed. Look around you at the bustling crowds and pay attention to the way different people move, stand, gesticulate and converse. Try and imagine how this would all appear if you were a visitor from another planet and had never before seen buildings, traffic or people. When you are able to focus intensely on the visual aspects of your surroundings for around two minutes at a time, change your emphasis from looking to listening.

One exercise I find helpful is based on the old saying 'to know something like the back of your hand'. In fact the majority of us have absolutely no clear idea what the back of either of our two hands really looks like. If you don't believe me try and describe either of them to yourself right now – obviously without cheating by taking a peep! What marks are there on your skin? Is the skin smooth or wrinkled? What do your knuckles look like, or your nails? Are both hands identical in appearance or do they differ in some way. Study them carefully for a few moments and try to observe them in a way you may never have done in the past. You'll find it an intriguing exercise.

Exercise 2: Developing Your Auditory Sense

Explore sounds as carefully and intently as possible. Notice those at a distance and those closer at hand. Observe how they rise and fall, change, blend and merge into one another. Focus all your attention on your sense of hearing and, if safe to do so, close your eyes to avoid being distracted by the images. While listening in this way try and avoid labelling any of the sounds you can hear. For example instead of thinking: 'Ah, an aircraft passing high overhead' or 'a dog barking close by', allow your brain to attend to their tonal quality and aural 'colour'. Once again use your own body as a 'sounding board' while lying quietly in bed at night. Focus on the sound of your breathing and, without making any judgement about it or labelling it as, for instance, smooth or laboured, just listen to it. How does it sound when it enters and leaves your body? Are there any differences in the sound of an inhalation and exhalation?

Exercise 3: Developing Your Sense of Smell

When you feel comfortable about being able to focus on sights and sounds at will, turn your attention to the different aromas around you while now paying as little attention as possible to anything else. Once again it will probably help you maintain intense focus if you close your eyes.

Distinguish between the various scents in the surrounding air and, as with the sounds, try to get out of the habit of putting a label on them or coming to some value judgement about them, such as 'that's a pleasant pine smell' or 'what a horrible stench of motor exhaust'. Remain as neutral and non-judgemental as possible.

Although we may only become aware of odours when especially pleasant or repugnant, they can still frequently exert a profound influence over our behaviour often without our ever being consciously aware of their effect. By triggering memories and emotional associations buried deep within the limbic system they can alter our mood and change our behaviour from one moment to the next. Perhaps one of the most famous examples in literature is how the smell and taste of lime tea and a madeleine cake led French novelist Marcel Proust to write his massive autobiographical novel *In Search of Times*

Past, by evoking overwhelmingly powerful memories of his childhood.

In my own clinical experience I recall one woman who developed a profound hatred of her mother-in-law at their very first meeting. Since the lady was gentle, charming and extremely kind this response was both inexplicable and damaging to the relationship with her husband. Under hypnosis the mystery was solved when it emerged that she had, as a very small child, been cruelly treated when staying with an aunt while her parents were overseas. This mean and abusive woman had used lavender water and this was exactly the same perfume as used by her mother-in-law. Although she had long repressed the memory of her unhappiness between the ages of twelve months and two years, the scent triggered a potent yet apparently irrational dread and loathing of the older woman at their very first meeting. Once the problem had been identified she was able to remove this b-lock and the two rapidly developed a warm and friendly relationship.

One reason for the power that odours of all kinds have as memory joggers is that, unlike information being sent from the eyes and ears, signals from the millions of scent detectors lining our nasal passages pass directly to the brain. Perhaps because of this our memory for smells is more powerful than for most other information. Research has shown that people can distinguish between odours smelled thirty days previously with 70 per cent accuracy. This compares with an accuracy of only about 10 per cent for visual and auditory information over the same period. So never ignore your sense of smell during sensualization training. Skill in recalling the scents associated with a particular event will enhance both the realism of that scene and recall of memories associated with it. Remember too that both memories and our sensations of odour are processed in the limbic system, which means a smell can often be responsible for first creating and then triggering a b-lock.

Exercise 4: Developing Your Sense of Taste

Carry out this exercise whenever eating or drinking. Again it may help if you close your eyes as you focus on the different sensations produced. Notice not only the taste but the changing texture and consistency of the food as you move it around in your mouth.

Taste and smell are, of course, very closely associated, although our olfactory system is around 25,000 times more sensitive than the sense of taste, as judged by the concentrations which can be detected.

If you have ever seen a map of the tongue in a textbook which showed taste buds that detect sweet things at the tip and bitter tastes at the back then forget it. All these widely published maps are wrong and based on a misinterpretation of the work of a nineteenth century German researcher. The fact is that any taste bud, which occur in onion-shaped clusters of between 50 to 100 in bumps on the tongue called papillae, is able to perceive any one of five flavours, sweet, sour, salty, bitter and *umami*. The final one, only recently identified and named after the Japanese for 'delicious', has a sort of Parmesan cheese flavour. When we extol the virtues of gourmet cooking, therefore, what we are actually talking about is not so much the taste as the subtle aromas of the food. Chemicals in the food are released by chewing and evaporate up into the nose via the throat.

Including taste sensations in your sensualization training will not only help you create more powerful virtual reality fantasies, it will also prove of great advantage when removing certain types of b-lock. If attempting to overcome acute anxiety caused by eating in public for instance (a common phobia), being able to taste the meal as you sensualize a meal with others will make it far easier for you to create a rounded recreation in your mind's eye.

Exercise 5: Developing Your Sense of Touch

Although you can carry out this exercise for enhancing the sense of touch almost anywhere, by focusing on signals from fingers and hands there will clearly be certain situations in which these sensations are especially powerful – as you get into a hot bath or stand under a shower, for example, while walking barefoot through grass or over sand, when making a snowball with bare hands or stroking the coat of an animal, and so on.

When picking something up try and notice how your fingers respond to the texture. Does it feel rough or smooth, silky or oily, hard or soft? Close your eyes and trace around the outline of your features with your fingertips. What do the contours of your face feel like? What about the surface of your skin? Smooth beneath your touch or rough and weathered? What do the lobes of your ears, the shape of your nose, your chin, forehead and hair feel like? Trace your fingers around your lips – are they full or narrow, dry or moist?

Exercise 6: Developing Your Kinaesthetic Sense

This will be of special interest and importance to those who take part in a sport and want to improve their performance or give themselves a competitive advantage.

Kinaesthetic sense, which élite athletes, gymnasts, acrobats, dancers, actors and mime artists possess to a very high degree, refers to a sense of what is going on inside your body. By turning your focus inwards and noticing what happens when sitting, lying, standing or moving you will build up a much better picture of your biodynamics, that is, how you use the more than 200 bones and 600 muscles of which your body is constructed. You will also be able to pick up needless tensions, especially in the muscles of the face.

Check now – is your forehead wrinkled or smoothed out? Are your back teeth clenched? Is your tongue resting loosely in your mouth? How are you sitting; what is happening inside the muscles of your lower back and shoulders? When moving around try and observe which groups of muscles are contracting and which are relaxing. Remember muscles cannot 'push', they only 'pull' to make a movement. When 'slicing' the lemon in the earlier exercise, for instance, your biceps contracted while your triceps, at the back of your upper arm, relaxed as you raised the blade. Then, as you brought it down to slice the lemon, the triceps contracted while the biceps relaxed.

Not only is such bodily awareness essential when constructing a sensualization concerning a sporting activity or similar activity in which movement is all important, but it will also help you become more aware of any barriers you may unintentionally be erecting that prevent effective breathing.

When carrying out these training exercises, bear the following points in mind.

1. Don't be surprised or disappointed if at first you find it difficult to concentrate on any single sensation, since it is quite likely that unwanted thoughts will intrude. Should this happen, simply notice you were distracted before calmly returning to the exercise. After a while these intrusive ideas will gradually decrease until you are able to focus all your attention to the sense being trained.
2. Try not to categorize or label any of the sights, sounds, smells and so on as you attend to them. Merely notice them in as neutral a manner as possible.
3. Do not evaluate the information, at this stage, as pleasant or unpleasant, attractive or unattractive. Just experience the sensation as objectively as you are able.

4. At first you can practise focusing on different sensations in various locations. Once you have gained some experience the next task is to take just one scene – preferably somewhere you find relaxing and agreeable – and explore it thoroughly using each of the six senses in turn. Then, during relaxation training (See Chapter Thirteen: Procedure Three) you can, if you wish, use that scene rather than the one I provide. You may find this helps you relax even better than my 'off the peg' sensualization as it contains memories very special and personal to yourself.

5. It is important not be become part of a sensualization in the sense of watching yourself as if performing in a movie. Always see events through your own eyes, hear them through your ears, touch, smell and taste them via your senses just as you would if there in real life.

6. After each exercise carry out another analysis using the rating scales provided. If you had difficulty conjuring up certain features, with a clarity rating of 3 or less, return to the real-life scene as soon as possible to enhance your memory. Focus mainly on those sensations which, although they formed an important part of the original scene, were poorly recalled during the sensualization.

While Sensualizing

* Be specific. You must see yourself carrying out some particular activity.

* Create surroundings and events in your mind's eye that are as vivid as you can make them. Use sights, sounds, taste, touch and smell.

* Perceive everything from your own viewpoint rather than from the position of a detached observer watching yourself in action. You are the key actor in this drama of the mind, not a member of the audience.

* If you start getting unduly anxious, switch scenes immediately

and return to the relaxing breath procedure taught in Chapter Thirteen.

- If you are uncertain of exactly how you want to act in a particular situation, rehearse several different versions. You might be assertive in one and less dominant in another for example. Imagine how others present are likely to respond to your various approaches and then consider your own responses to them.

- At first you may find that your sensualizations are not as clear or as easily sustained as you wish them to be. You may also start feeling unhelpfully anxious almost as soon as you picture yourself in the stressful situation, but with a little practice you should find it perfectly possible to create and sustain powerful mirrors of real-life events. Initial anxiety quickly declines with each repetition of the scene, allowing you to deal in a relaxed and confident manner with even the most stressful of challenges. Then when you come to attempt them in real life this rehearsal will help you keep your fears under control.

- Once you are able to cope confidently while sensualizing a challenge you will be ready to deal with it in real life.

The Benefits of Sensualization Training

By learning how to maximize all your senses when creating sensualization you will:

- Significantly improve your powers of observation.
- Provide yourself with a storehouse of accurate memories that may be used for creating further sensualizations.
- Sharpen your senses. Like everything else in the human body, these organs function best when used regularly. To keep sight, hearing, smell, taste and touch in prime condition they need to be exercised frequently.

- Enhance your powers of mental focus. This will, in turn, enhance your performance in virtually every mental and physically demanding activity. Indeed the difference between a great thinker and a good thinker, or a supreme sports person and a merely highly competent one can often be found in their abilities to concentrate intently on the task at hand.

The cumulative benefits of all these is an ability to see the world as it really is rather than as you might wish or fear it to be.

Remember that much of the incoming information from your eyes, ears and other sensory apparatus is being edited by your limbic and other areas low down in the brain before passing into that very limited sphere of attention we call consciousness. This means that, especially when any b-locks are present, you become essentially deaf and blind to situations, circumstances or events as they actually are and perceive them instead through filters of self-delusion. The result is all too often FEAR, or False Evidence Appearing Real.

Jason, the public-speaking phobic whose story I told in Chapters One and Two, did not actually see his audience at all. Rather his limbic system filtered and adjusted his visual perceptions so that the only expressions he could see where those that matched his memory of the faces of his father and the farm workers. The result was, of course, an abrupt move to the right of the O-Zone with an inevitable decline in his performance.

Equally, incoming information may be interpreted in an overly positive and unrealistic way, causing us to miss important warning signs alerting us to a need to make changes. This can lead you to perceiving challenges not as they really are but as you would wish them to be. Accurate observation, using all your senses, enables you to form far more accurate judgements about the world around you than would otherwise be possible.

Once you are able to sensualize easily, proceed to Part Two of this book. Here I will explain the six procedures involved in breakthrough breathwork. After reading Chapter Nine, which offers basic guidance on how best to use the six training programmes taught, move directly to your area of most pressing need, that aspect of your life where some b-lock is preventing you from remaining within your O-Zone when performing some crucially important activity.

Summary of Chapter Nine

- Many athletes and sportsmen use visual imagery to help them improve their performance and give them a competitive edge.
- Images work powerfully not only on our ideas and emotions, they can also affect the way we respond physically.
- Visualizing a particular activity results in the same electrical impulses being sent to the muscles involved as would happen were that action really occurring.
- The language of the limbic system in which b-locks arise involves images as well as other basic sensory responses such as smell, touch and taste.
- By using all five senses to create or recreate a situation in which you are currently having difficulties it becomes far easier to eliminate these barriers to performance.
- Sensualization is an ability that we all, to varying degrees, possess and which can easily and quickly be perfected.
- The starting point is to focus more closely and intently on just one sensory element – such as sights or sounds – in the world around you.
- Begin with the one that comes most easily – for many this is the visual sense – before moving in turn to all the remainder.

Part Two

MASTERING BASIC BREATHWORK

'Prana is the infinite all pervading energy of the universe ...
One who has learned to control prana has learned to control
all the energies of this universe – physical and mental. He has
also learned to control his body and mind.'

SWAMI RAMA *PORTAL TO HIGHER AWARENESS: THE SCIENCE
OF BREATH*

CHAPTER TEN

Making a start with breakthrough breathwork

You can master most of the practical training procedures taught in this part of the book by working with each one for no more than three minutes twice a day. The first two procedures (building core stability and deep diaphragmatic breathing), which form the foundation for breakthrough breathwork, need to be practised first and will take a little longer – even so they need not involve more than a single session lasting around ten minutes a day. For some, the early morning soon after waking up proves the best time since it refreshes and strengthens them for the rest of the day. For others the end of the day is better as it helps banish much of the stress and pressures that have built up while working, so enabling them to enjoy a more relaxed and restful period of recuperation before going to bed. It is a small investment of your time that will pay big dividends in terms of your future well–being and enhanced potential for achievement.

Once you have learned these two basic procedures, which of the four others you decide to acquire will depend on your specific circumstances. If for example your current difficulties concern stress and achieving greater focus at work or when playing a sport, you may wish only to become proficient with Procedures Three (Chapter Thirteen) and Five (Chapter Fifteen). If you are finding your progress blocked by some psychological barriers, such as intense anxiety or unreasonable outbursts of anger, then you will want to work with Procedure Six (Chapter Sixteen).

Once you have become proficient with each of these, if they are not being used regularly to deal with actual difficulties, you should keep them fresh in your mind with two or three practice sessions per week. Restricting your initial training to these limited periods of time makes it far easier to maintain regular, daily practice no matter how hectic your schedule becomes.

Building knowledge step-by-step means that when starting on a new day's training the procedure practised on the preceding day remains fresh in your mind. Even so small an amount of time will be sufficient to provide a sound basic understanding of the essentially very simple breathwork required to produce a desired mental state. When you then need to switch into the same state of mind to deal with a specific intellectual or physical challenge you should be able to do so smoothly and efficiently, in just three minutes.

Suppose, for instance, you want to relax deeply and fully to combat rising stress. You would spend the first 30 seconds using Procedure Two (deep diaphragmatic breathing) taught in Chapter Twelve. This will help you unwind generally, so preparing your mind and body for the Relaxing Breath. This will take 90 seconds during which you will breathe according to the pattern described in Procedure Three (Chapter Thirteen).

Having established the specific pattern of brain activity in which the relaxation sensualization works best, you would then spend the final 60 seconds recreating that scene in your mind's eye. At this point you should find that your stress and anxiety have either disappeared entirely or significantly diminished in intensity. In their place is a tranquil yet receptive alertness, a state of mind and body in which you can calmly and confidently deal with any challenges that lie ahead.

Even if you have been a long-time user of breathwork techniques, for instance as a student of yoga, I feel sure you will still derive great benefit from the procedures taught in *Breathe Easy*. If you are new to procedures based on breathing and sensualizing you may find, as many of our clients already have, that this new knowledge will actually change your life. Within a very short space of time you will be in possession of sufficient practical insights into your mechanisms of breathing, and sufficiently familiar with the basic techniques, to use whichever one is most appropriate for dealing with a particular problem. You will find that the six powerful procedures taught in this easily followed programme are sufficient to help you break through barriers to achievement and so realize your true potential.

A Note of Caution

Although all the breathing procedures I describe are easy to perform and must be carried out in a relaxed manner, if you have:

* Any current problems with your breathing.
* Suffer from a condition such as asthma or emphysema.
* Have high blood pressure or a heart condition.
* Are recovering from chest or abdominal surgery.
* Or have any other reason to suggest changes in your pattern of breathing could prove hazardous ...

please seek professional medical guidance before continuing.

An Overview of the Procedures

Chapter Eleven – Procedure One: Developing Core Stability

The primary goal of this first part of the programme is to create a strong core control centre. This forms the starting point for all the exercises that follow, allowing you to free up your breathing by safely stretching and strengthening the area around your abdomen. Core centring will also enable you to take advantage of your body's centre of gravity which lies just behind the navel, close to the third or fourth lumbar vertebra.

Your abdominal muscles, especially the transverse abdominis, help to protect the lumbar spine. You will learn how to lengthen this part of the backbone and correct the placement of your pelvis and spine so that they assume a neutral position, so greatly assisting both postural and breathing efficiency.

Time required 6 minutes daily five times a week.

Chapter Twelve – Procedure Two: Deep Diaphragmatic Breathing

During this part of the training I will be showing you how to explore the basic mechanisms of your breathing together with practising the most fundamental and important of all breathing skills – deep diaphragmatic breathing. This is the most basic breathwork procedure and the foundation on which mental and physical well-being is built.

For reasons explained in Chapter Six, by using your powerful diaphragm muscle when taking in or expelling a breath air is drawn deep into the lowest portions of the lungs. This ensures ample supplies of oxygen are extracted for use by brain and body while carbon dioxide is efficiently expelled.

Time required 6 minutes daily for one week.

Chapter Thirteen – Procedure Three: The Relaxing Breath

This is the pattern of breathing to adopt whenever the stresses and strains of daily life increase levels of mental and physical arousal to the point where you start moving to the right of the arousal curve and out of your O-Zone. Having relaxed your body you will then learn how to unwind your mind using an appropriate sensualization. You will find that this breathwork procedure enables you to relax mind and body quickly and easily, in most instances enabling you to return to your O–Zone inside two minutes.

Time required two sessions a day, each of around 3 minutes.

Chapter Fourteen – Procedure Four: The Energizing Breath

As the name implies, this increases energy and vitality in any situation where your mental and physical levels are sharply decreasing, causing you to shift away from your O–Zone towards the left side of the arousal/performance curve. You should spend a few moments working with this procedure whenever the need arises to overcome fatigue and reinvigorate mind and body. You will find it especially beneficial after a lengthy period of intense brain work, especially when this has involved little or no physical activity and required you to keep your gaze fixed at a specific distance – for example after a spell at the computer.

Time required two sessions a day each of around 3 minutes.

Chapter Fifteen – Procedure Five: The Focused Breath

As with the two previous procedures, this will enable you to produce a state of mind in which your brain is highly receptive to rehearsing mentally any demanding physical or mental activity. However, unlike the breakthrough procedure taught in Procedure Six its purpose is not to remove unconscious mental barriers to peak performance but to sharpen your powers of concentration on which achievement often depends. It could, for example, be used by a golfer to practise his or her swing, a businessperson who wants to stay in control of an intellectually demanding activity, or someone needing to maintain a high level of concentration, for instance while attending a job interview or promotions' board.

After you have created the ideal mental state by means of this breathing procedure you will then use sensualization to go through every aspect of the forthcoming challenge in your mind's eye.

Time required two sessions a day, each of around 3 minutes.

Chapter Sixteen – Procedure Six: Breakthrough Breathing

In this final chapter you will learn a pattern of breathing designed to bring about a state of mind in which your brain can more easily and effectively remove any emotional b-locks that may currently prevent you from remaining within your O-Zone when attempting specific activities of importance to you. These may include such challenges as asserting yourself during a confrontation, making a presentation before a group of people, playing a competitive sport, going out on a first date and so on.

This programme involves three stages:

Stage One: Identifying the b-lock. Time required one 6-minute session a day.

Stage Two: Mastering the breathwork procedure. Time required two sessions daily, each of 3 minutes.

Stage Three: Eliminating the b-lock. Time required varies, usually one session a day lasting around 5 minutes until such time as the barrier has been eliminated permanently from your unconscious.

How to Proceed

Whatever your particular reason for using any of these breathwork procedures, the starting point should always be to practise the core stability exercises described in Procedure One before proceeding to master the deep diaphragmatic breathing taught in Procedure Two. At the same time you can, if you wish, start working on one of the five remaining procedures, depending on your current needs.

Although it is perfectly possible to carry out the training required for Procedures Three to Six virtually anywhere you will find it easier to learn the first two procedures *only* under the following conditions:

- Lie on a firm surface, such as a carpeted floor. If lying on any other surface you will be more comfortable using a mat, thick towel or blanket under you.
- Wear a light-weight and loose fitting outfit whenever possible since tight clothing restricts your breathing. If wearing your everyday clothes loosen belt and tie or any other breath and movement restricting clothing.
- Ideally use a room which is warm – but not too hot – and reasonably quiet where you can perform the exercises in private.
- Try and avoid any interruptions during your 3 minutes of training. I suggest you disconnect the telephone and tactfully but firmly insist on being left alone to focus on the procedure you're learning.
- Finally, since it is obviously impossible to read and follow these instructions at the same time, my advice is to read through them a couple of times while studying the relevant illustrations.

With the book close at hand for easy reference, mentally go through the instructions, carrying out the actions involved as accurately as you can remember them. If you get stuck, then check back with the text. After a couple of such rehearsals there should be little or no difficulty in working through the whole exercise.

A Word About the Sensualizations

In procedures Three, Four and Five, once you have brought the brain into the required mental state by using the pattern of breathing described, I am going to ask you to use a sensualization that involves creating your own private personal paradise where no harm can ever befall you. I suggest that you begin by working with my descriptions and then modify or change the details to suit your own personal preferences. Occasionally, however, I have clients who dislike and cannot work with the island sensualization, perhaps because they hate or fear water, or are intimidated by the thought of solitude. If this applies to you then I suggest you work with a scenario with which you feel entirely comfortable. As suggested in Chapter Nine, you can gather information for such a scene while carrying out your sensualization training. Some people, for example, prefer to sensualize themselves in a beautiful garden or a quiet and tranquil country meadow.

The precise nature of the sensualization you choose is not important. What does matter is that all your five senses are involved.

You must:

- **See** everything that happens through your own eyes.
- **Hear** all the sounds through your own ears.
- **Taste, touch and smell** your surroundings.
- **Feel** the way your own body moves in that situation, as well as sensations such as warmth or cold, moisture or dryness on the skin, the touch of grass against your legs or the softness of sand beneath your feet.

Always keep in mind that sensualizing is not the same as visualizing. It makes this already powerful process even more potent and effective by allowing you to create a virtual reality within your mind that in every respect mirrors the reality of actual experience.

Finally, for Procedure Six you will be using a very different sensualization and one that I shall describe in detail in Chapter Sixteen.

So now, let's make a start. Set aside 6 minutes during which you can begin to build excellent core stability – the basis of healthy, optimal breathing for healthy, optimal living.

CHAPTER ELEVEN

Procedure One: developing core stability

The purpose of the following exercises is to strengthen the muscles surrounding your abdomen and trunk in order to enhance what is termed core stability.

Core stability refers to the control you are able to exert over the muscles surrounding your stomach and the manner in which they interact with muscles in your trunk and lower extremities. It is also the key to balance since our centre of gravity is located directly behind the navel, opposite the third or fourth lumbar vertebrae, and is the point from which most movements are initiated. These include even mundane actions such as standing up from a seated position, getting out of bed, reaching beyond arm's length, walking or running. Balance is, of course, even more crucial when performing any of the high-intensity movements present in a majority of sports.

Think of Your Body as a Chain

One way of understanding the importance of core stability is to think of your body as a multi-linked chain comprising the feet, ankles, legs, knees, hips, trunk, shoulders, arms, wrists and hands. Delivering power through this chain – such as when you stoop to pick up a load – requires that each link is strong, especially at the trunk, the connecting point of our lower and upper body. Even one weak link in this chain means that the performance of the whole system is impaired with power and efficiency being scarified. This is especially true when that weakest link is located – as it so often is – at the central connecting point.

Whenever you use the wrong muscles when transferring force from your arms and legs through your pelvic girdle to your spine, or if the appropriate muscles are used but these are relatively weak, your body will seek a way to compensate for the subsequent imbalance. This is usually achieved by using other muscles that are often ill-suited to the demands of that particular movement, which can lead to a sacrifice of power and efficiency combined with greater risk of such injuries as shoulder tendonitis and low back, or lumbar, pain.

Problems in this region of the spine are now widespread in the developed world and are one of the main causes for taking time off work. By improving your core stability, then, you will help safeguard your spine or, if already suffering such low back pain, reduce or eliminate current discomfort.

In addition, and most importantly for this breakthrough breathwork training programme, core stability is essential for smooth, easy and efficient breathing.

Breathing and Core Stability

A strong yet flexible corset of muscles at the core of your body will help to ensure the diaphragm can move powerfully and freely when drawing air into the lungs and then expelling it again.

The reasons why core stability yields such benefits are easily appreciated if you consider the two different postures that result first from a weak and then from a strong girdle of muscles around our middle. In the first case the individual is likely to be slumped somewhat forward, especially if their abdominal muscles are significantly stronger than are those in their back. This is often found among body builders, whose 'six-pack' stomachs, while admired by women and envied by other men, result in impaired breathing.

The generally poor core stability found among people who take little or no exercise is often worsened if they are overweight. This makes it virtually impossible for them to draw in the deep diaphragmatic breath described in the next chapter – breathwork that is your essential passport to good health and maximum vitality.

Someone who has developed strong yet flexible muscles at their core and is at the correct weight for their height is far more likely to have an upright posture that allows air to flow smoothly into their lungs and be able to use their powerful diaphragm muscle to the full.

By developing greater core stability, therefore, you will be able to:

* Breathe far more efficiently and effectively.
* Reduce your risk of injury, especially to the lower back.
* Use all your muscles more efficiently.
* Improve your balance and co-ordination.
* Enhance your posture.
* Avoid wasting energy.

The Myth of the 'Six-Pack' Stomach

Read any modern health or fitness magazine and you are likely to find a great many articles describing ways of developing only one of the abdominal muscles, the rectus abdominis, responsible for the 'six-pack' stomach and illustrated on the next page.

Rectus Abdominis

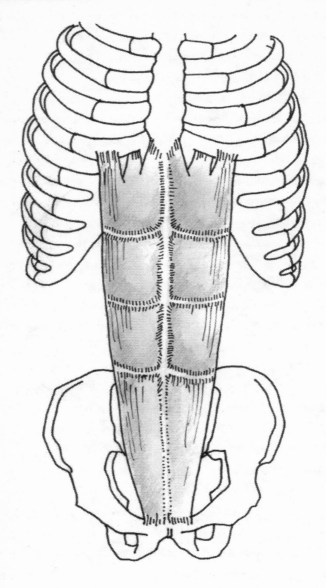

The rectus abdominis muscle responsible for the much admired and –
by many men – much envied 'six-pack' stomach.

The reason for all this interest is that by strengthening the rectus abdominis you can produce the rippling 'six-pack' effect that many men and women have, quite wrongly, come to regard as an outward and visible symbol of physical fitness. In their quest for the ideal stomach millions of males – and to a lesser extent females – spend many disagreeable hours each week performing crunches, sit-ups and leg lifts. Unfortunately the most probable outcome of all this sweating and straining is a minor increase in abdominal strength together with a minimal reduction in their waistline. Others purchase so called 'ab machines' which promise to build a stomach to be proud of with little or no effort. Unfortunately recent research by sports physiologists at San Diego State University has shown that use of two of the most popular machines, the ab rocker and ab roller, provides the least effective of any type of abdominal exercise. They used a technique called electromyography to measure electrical activity in the abdominal muscles and so discovered which were doing the work during a variety of exercises. They found that while all the traditional or popular abdominal exercises worked the right muscles, some did significantly better than others. One of the best, the 'supine bicycle' is described below.

However, bear in mind that while developing strong abdominals is part of the story it is by no means the whole story. Indeed the widespread belief in the health enhancing attributes of the 'six-pack' stomach stems from two popular but mistaken notions about the benefits of keeping one's stomach muscles under tension. The first mistake is to assume, as many do, that by relaxing your stomach muscles you make your belly bigger. The second error is to assume that by keeping the abdominal muscles tight you will help avoid low back pain. The only outcomes of both these assumptions is to impair breathing, while at the same time undermining core stability. As breathing specialist Donna Farhi comments: 'The simple fact is that holding the abdominal muscles in a constant state of contraction causes them to *weaken*. In order for any muscle to function effectively it has to completely relax between contractions ... relaxing your abdomen doesn't mean letting it hang out in a completely flaccid state; it means letting your belly move so that you experience both the relaxation and tonus phase of the breath cycle.' As for safeguarding your spine by tightening your abdominal muscles, a more likely outcome is to *increase* the risk of low back pain by producing greater tension and stiffness around the spine.

What matters is not a six- or more accurately an eight-pack stomach but the all round strength and flexibility that comes from developing good core stability.

The Muscles that Contribute to Your Core Stability

Over emphasis on the rectus abdominis (six-pack) tends to obscure the fact that there are three additional and equally important abdominal muscles each with a different action and function, all of which contribute equally to core stability. These are:

* The internal obliques
* The external obliques
* The transversus abdominis

People who spend a great deal of time struggling to strengthen these muscles by standard sit-ups or perhaps sit-ups with a twist, fail to work on the most important abdominal muscles of all – the transversus abdominis. Located at the mid-section of the body's torso, it encompasses the lower back and abdominal area, wrapping around the entire trunk wall and inserting into the tissues (fascia) covering the spine. This muscle plays a primary role in keeping the lumbar spine and pelvis stable during movement.

Core Stability Muscles

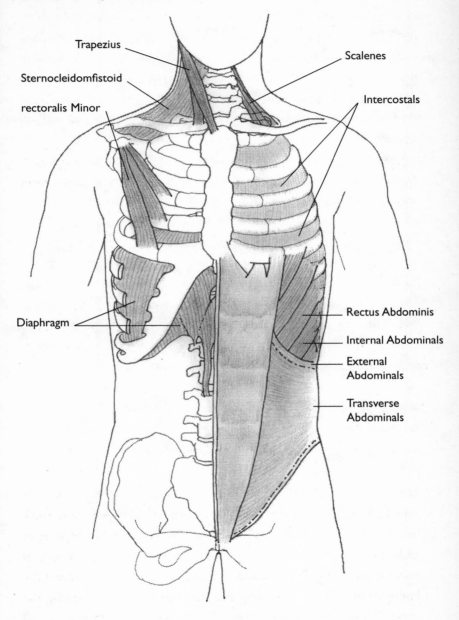

Trapezius

Sternocleidomfistoid

rectoralis Minor

Scalenes

Intercostals

Diaphragm

Rectus Abdominis

Internal Abdominals

External Abdominals

Transverse Abdominals

To appreciate why basic sit-up exercises can never completely develop core strength, compare the core of your body to a container with a front, back and two sides. Core stability demands you strengthen all four walls of this container; that is the muscles in both your abdominal region and your lower back: the multifidii, quadratus lumborum, longissimus and illiocostalis.

It is equally important, however, to develop flexibility as well as strength since flexible muscles are better able to lengthen and stretch in order to meet the demands placed on them. When carrying out the exercise described below, pay great attention to your technique as the quality of any exercise is of greater importance than the quantity. Rather than pushing yourself to complete a certain number of repetitions, focus on performing each exercise in as slow and controlled a manner as possible. By doing so you will ensure that only the specific muscle the particular exercise is designed to strengthen is being worked on. At the same time a slow, focused attitude will help you achieve far greater awareness of these core muscles.

Below you will find six exercises that will significantly enhance your core stability. These easily mastered techniques won't even cause you to work up a sweat. They are all that is needed to ensure healthy and health promoting muscles around the middle of your body.

A Word Before You Begin

These exercises are easy to master and can be done with little effort. However, as is customary in any book suggesting physical exercises to a wide public, I do ask you to seek medical advice if you are:

- Overweight.
- Pregnant.
- Have high blood pressure or a heart condition.
- Have spinal problems, such as low back pain.

- Have recently had surgery, especially to your stomach or back.
- Suffer from any medical condition such that exercises could make matters worse.
- If in any doubt about the suitability of these exercises ask for a medical opinion before proceeding.
- When carrying out the exercises do so slowly and carefully, concentrating on getting each action as near perfect as possible.
- Take especial care when standing up after the exercises are completed.
- If you start feeling giddy or breathless while doing any of these exercises then stop immediately and wait until you regain your breath and/or your balance.

Six Ways to Enhance Your Core Stability

Core Stability Exercises

1. Supine Bicycle

Time required: 60 seconds

1. Lie on your back with your hands behind your head and legs bent to 45 degrees.
2. Use a cycling motion to bring your right leg first to your left and then to your right elbow.
3. Return your right leg to the starting position then repeat with the left leg, bringing the left knee first to the left and then to the right elbow.
4. Repeat eight times for each leg.
5. If at first you find it difficult to manage eight repetitions for each leg then do as many as you feel comfortable with and build up to eight.

This concludes Exercise 1. Pause for a few moments before moving to the next exercise.

2. Back Strengthening

Time required: 60 seconds

1. Lie on your back with your knees bent, feet one hip-width apart and parallel, your arms resting either on your lower abdomen or at your side, as illustrated below.
2. You may find it more comfortable to rest your head on a small, flat, firm pillow. Shut your eyes or keep them open, whichever feels more comfortable for you.
3. Start by relaxing your stomach muscles so that you can take a long, slow, deep breath and, as you exhale, flatten the small of your back against the floor.
4. Arch the small of your back during the inhalation and count slowly to five as you do so. As you exhale repeat the slow count to five as you lower and flatten your back against the floor again.
5. Repeat SIX times.
6. Now breathe in, slightly arching the small of your back and then, as you breath out, allow the area around and below your navel to soften and 'hollow out' towards the spine. It may help, at first, to imagine that you are lying in a hammock. Hold your muscles in this hollowed position and feel how your lower spine lengthens.
7. Breathe in again and relax the muscles. Repeat FIVE times.

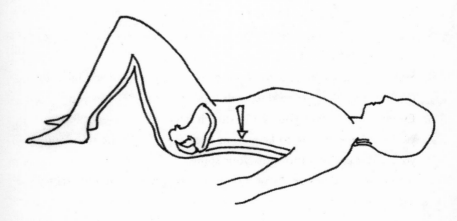

This concludes the second core stability exercise. Pause for a few moments before proceeding to Exercise 3.

3. Spine Lengthening

Time required: 60 seconds

1. While still lying flat on the floor with your knees bent, feet one hip-width apart and parallel, arms resting at your side, take in a long, slow, deep breath.
2. As you slowly begin to exhale, hollow out your lower abdominal muscles by pulling your navel back towards your spine. Feel the muscles tightening and wrapping themselves around your middle like a corset.

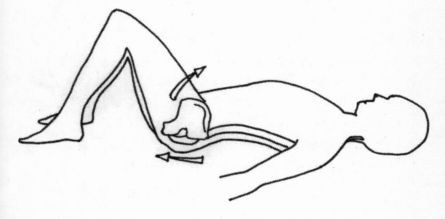

3. Now gently lengthen the lower part of your spine while keeping it pressed flat against the floor.
4. Still slowly exhaling, slide your right leg along the floor and lift your right arm above your head so as to touch the floor behind you.
5. Enjoy the feeling as you gently stretch from your fingertips to your toes but be sure to keep your back flat against the floor and your navel pulled in towards your spine.
6. Inhale slowly and deeply as you return your right arm and right leg to the starting position.

7. Repeat these movements using your left arm and leg, stretching them as before.

8. Repeat FIVE times for each side of the body, making a total of TEN repetitions.

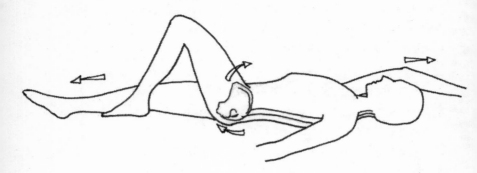

This concludes core stability exercise 3. Pause for a moment before proceeding to the fourth exercise.

Points to Remember

* Do not over-tighten your stomach muscles – try to hollow them out while keeping them loose.
* Your tailbone should remain flat on the floor as you gently stretch and lengthen the spine.
* Avoid allowing your back to arch as you stretch and lengthen your arms and legs.
* When pulling your navel in towards the spine always simultaneously lengthen your spine. These two actions must go hand in hand, for an elongated spine supported by strong abdominals is essential for good posture and good health.
* It is also important not to raise your bottom from the floor. Never push your spine down hard or tighten the muscles around your hips.

4. Gentle Stomach Tightening

Time required: 60 seconds

One problem encountered by people with poorly toned muscles is that their abdominal muscles have a strong tendency to 'bowstringing' outwards as they walk around, allowing their guts to sag. This not only puts unnecessary strain on the spine but also makes it impossible to take a deep diaphragmatic breath that I shall teach you in the next chapter. To prevent this happening use the following exercise:

1. Start in a kneeling position as shown in the illustration below.
2. Keeping your spine motionless, allow your abdominal muscles to sag towards the floor.
3. Now tighten these muscles so as to 'hollow' your abdomen.
4. Focus your attention on pulling the tummy button up and in.
5. Hold this tension for a slow count to FIVE, then release.
6, Repeat TWELVE times.

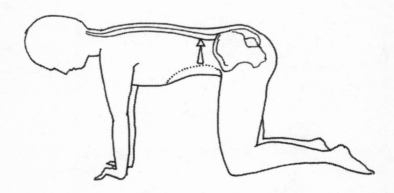

This concludes core stability exercise 4. Once again I suggest you pause for a moment before moving to Exercise 5.

5. Legs Raised Chest Lift

Time required: 60 seconds

1. For this exercise you will need a chair, stool or similar support.
2. Lie on your back and use the chair or similar support to raise your legs into a 90-degree bend as illustrated below.
3. Your legs should be bent at both the hips and the knees.
4. Place your hands at your sides with the palms flat on the ground.
5. Your head and neck should be held as straight as possible as you lift the front of your chest towards the ceiling.
6. Make certain you are bending at the hips and not the neck.
7. Imagine yourself being drawn upwards by an invisible cord.
8. As you raise your head and shoulders off the floor, slide your hands forward.
9. Do not attempt to lift yourself more than a few inches and make certain you are only using your stomach muscles to pull yourself up.
10. Inhale slowly and deeply as you begin to raise yourself.
11. Hold this position for a count to three then slowly lower yourself again exhaling as you do so.
12. Repeat FIVE times.

This concludes core stability exercise 5. Pause for a moment before moving to the final set of exercises.

6. Back Strengthening

Time required: 60 seconds

This final exercise will help you strengthen the muscles of your back:

1. Lie face down with your arms stretched straight out in front of you, palms flat on the floor as shown below.
2. Inhale slowly and, as you begin doing so, start walking your hands backwards towards you.
3. At the same time arch your spine slowly upwards until you can feel a gentle stretch in the lower back.
4. Exhale slowly while holding this position for FIVE seconds.
5. Repeat TWELVE times.

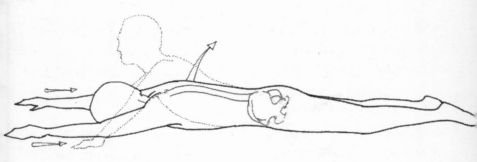

This concludes the six simple exercises that will help you build and maintain the excellent level of core stability on which good health and optimal breathwork so crucially depend. You can if you wish increase the number of repetitions for each exercise, provided, of course, that you never allow your technique to suffer as a result.

In the next chapter I will show you how to master the basic building block of all breathwork – deep diaphragmatic breathing.

CHAPTER TWELVE

Procedure Two: deep diaphragmatic breathing

Let's start with a simple experiment. I'd like you, right now, to stand up and take, then release, a deep breath. While doing so notice exactly what you are doing. If you are like the vast majority of people, while inhaling deeply you will probably have observed some or all of the following:

* It will have required an effort to take this breath and, with the test completed, you will quickly return to a more 'normal' pattern of breathing.
* You will have pulled your stomach strongly inwards while simultaneously thrusting your chest and spine forwards.
* The air will have been drawn into your body via a long, hard 'sniff' that causes your nostrils to draw together instead of remaining relaxed and flared.
* Your shoulders will have risen and fallen vertically rather than moving laterally in and out.

Not too sure what happened in your case? Then without making any changes to the way you inhale deeply repeat the exercise and notice how many of those four observations hold true. If all four provided an accurate description of what it means for you to inhale deeply, then your breathing is dysfunctional. But don't be too alarmed or upset – it is certainly no different from that found in the majority of people.

The surprising truth is that, as I explained in Chapter Seven, around seven out of ten of us spend most, if not all, our adult lives using inverted 'upside-down' breathing.

Are You an Upside-Down Breather?

The starting point is to discover the extent to which you already make use of abdominal breathing by carrying out a simple breath awareness test. Here's how to go about it:

1. Find a firm but giving surface on which to lie down, such as a carpeted floor or a thick towel.
2. Remove any heavy sweaters, waist-constricting belts, and any other clothing that might interfere with normal breathing patterns.
3. Now place one hand flat on your chest near the top of your breastbone and one on your stomach slightly above the navel.
4. Without changing your normal pattern of breathing in any way, notice which hand rises more when you are breathing in your normal way. Do you feel the greatest movement in your chest or in your stomach?
5. Does one hand rise before the other or do both seem to rise and fall in unison?
6. If your lower hand moves more than your upper then your breathing is abdominal or diaphragmatic.
7. If, as typically happens, your upper hand moves most then you are using costal or upside-down breathing.

If you found that you are already breathing diaphragmatically that's very good news indeed. The procedures taught in the remainder of this book will help you strengthen that healthy pattern of breathing while enhancing your understanding of the breath-mind relationship.

If you discovered that you are breathing upside-down there is no need to worry. This faulty habit is easily broken and, by starting to breathe in the way nature intended rather than the way life's pressures have imposed, you should rapidly notice a significant and dramatic improvement in your general well-being.

Exploring Your Breathing Machinery

- Lie or sit down with your arms resting by your sides and your feet about shoulder-width apart. You may feel more comfortable if you support your neck and head on a pillow.
- Start by becoming aware of your ribcage. Bring your hands up so that you can feel your collarbones (clavicles). Run your fingers along these bones to the point where they attach to your breastbone or sternum (see illustration on page 77).
- Now gently explore the area around the junction of the collarbone and sternum. The bone you can feel directly beneath the collarbone is your second rib, the first being tucked away beneath the collarbone.
- Trace your fingers along this rib starting at the shoulder and moving inwards towards the sternum. Note how it becomes increasingly prominent towards the point where it attaches to your sternum. Notice how firm and unyielding this attachment feels.
- Placing your fingers on the point at which the second rib attaches to your sternum, inhale deeply and note the slight movement. This shows that although a robust and solid protective structure your ribcage still has considerable flexibility.

- Take several more deep breaths and become aware of the way in which the ribcage expands with each inhalation and falls back again as you exhale.
- Slowly run your fingers down the breastbone and notice the way each of your ribs is attached to it. As your fingers move down the sternum you will find that the ribs become closer and closer together.
- At the far end of the sternum you should be able to feel a small prominence called the xiphoid process. This may well be very sensitive to the touch since it is attached to the diaphragm.
- Follow the outer boundaries of your ribcage with your fingers, noting how the lowest ribs extend right around your waist. Many people assume the lungs are located high in the chest, while they actually follow the structure of the ribcage.
- Now let your hands rest back at your sides while you mentally map out the same territory you have just been exploring with your fingers.
- In your mind's eye visualize how the collarbone connects to the sternum. See yourself travelling down the breastbone until you reach the xiphoid process.
- Next visualize the bottom of your ribcage from front to spine on both sides of your body. Create a mental image of the ribs extending around at about the level of your waist.
- As you take several deep breaths in and out, visualize the way your ribs are moving with each inhalation and exhalation.

It is important to build up this mental image of the basic movements of muscles and bones before starting any of the procedures, as it enables you to master and carry out all the remaining procedures.

For the second part of this first training session, we will combine this visualization with the practical movements involved in deep diaphragmatic breathing. Rather than performing the next set of exercises purely mechanically, therefore, I'd like you to 'see' what is going on inside your body by means of a carefully constructed 'mind movie'.

Practising Deep Diaphragmatic Breathing

Since healthy deep diaphragmatic breathing is most easily learned while lying down, that is how we will start. Later, when you become proficient, it will be necessary to learn ways of incorporating the same patterns of breath into your everyday life.

1. Start by lying on your back with your hands at your sides.
2. Flex your legs at the knees to approximately 45 degrees and place your feet a comfortable distance apart. Try to find a position that allows your body to feel relaxed and balanced. If at any time your legs become tired through holding them in this position, stretch them out for a moment or two before resuming your initial position.

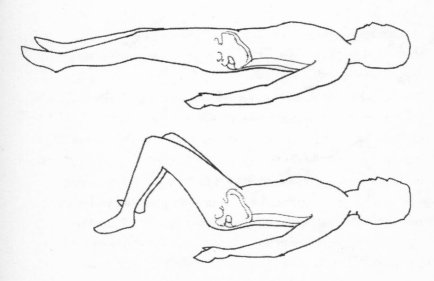

3. Now arch the small of your back and then flatten it against the floor beneath you. It is important that the movement is smooth and flowing, not short and erratic. Try to feel and sense the sensations of the movement as you arch and flatten the small of your back.

4. Repeat this procedure for approximately one minute.

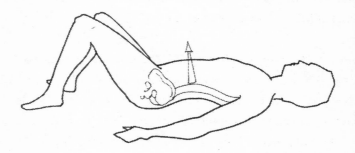

5. Inhale slowly and deeply, arching the small of your back as you do so.

6. Exhale deeply and slowly, at the same time flattening the small of your back.

7. To repeat: breathe in and fill your lungs as you arch the small of your back, then breathe out emptying your lungs as you flatten the small of your back against the floor.

8. It is essential to keep all your movements slow and fluid. It should never involve any great movement, only a few centimetres of arching and flattening the small of your back. (See Illustration 24.)

9. As you inhale repeat slowly and silently, 'I know that I am breathing in' and as you exhale say, 'I know that I am breathing out.' This will help you recognize your in-breath as an in-breath and your out-breath as an out-breath. You don't even need to recite the whole sentence. You can if you prefer simply repeat: 'in' and 'out'.

10. At the same time use the mind map you created of your breathing mechanism to follow the course of the air past your nostrils – notice how cool the incoming air feels compared to the expelled breath – and down into your lungs.

11. Visualize the air flowing deep into the lower lobes of each lung as your diaphragm is drawn smoothly downwards and outwards while your chest expands gently upwards and outwards. This visual imagery combined with the simple verbal instructions will make it far easier to keep your mind focused on your breathing.

12. By practising for between 2 and 5 minutes a day you should rapidly find that, as your breathing becomes more peaceful and gentle, your whole outlook will grow calmer and more relaxed.

From Practice to Daily Life

After practising deep diaphragmatic breathing in this way for a week to ten days you are ready to transfer your newly found skill from the classroom to the real world. This is, of course, essential if you are to rid yourself of the negative consequences of dysfunctional upside-down breathing.

Breaking any well-established pattern of behaviour is never easy. I remember world-class golfer Nick Faldo telling me of the years of struggle and effort that went into changing his golf stroke with the help of golfing mentor David Leadbetter. It is the same with altering habitual patterns of breathing. If you have been breathing upside-down since childhood, it will seem such a normal and natural way to take your breaths that making any substantial changes – no matter how beneficial and life-enhancing they prove – will require commitment and persistence.

There are two ways to approach this challenge. For the first you will need nothing more than an index card and for the second a small pocket timer. These can be bought cheaply from many hardware or electronics shops. Alternatively you can use those built into some watches and virtually all personal organizers.

Method One: Using a Cue Card

The first technique involves identifying six triggers that will remind you to spend a few moments focusing on your breathing, identifying how you are doing so and changing it – where necessary from upside-down to deep diaphragmatic breathing. Typical trigger points during the day might be:

1. While waiting to catch my bus/train each morning or while sitting in my car at traffic lights.
2. When I take a mid-morning break.
3. After making the third telephone call of the day.
4. While taking my lunch break.
5. On my way home.
6. When I sit down to watch TV.

These are then written down on the index card as a reminder during the first few days. Each time you reach a trigger point, stop. Turn your mind inwards for a moment or two and notice how you are taking and releasing each breath. Is your stomach moving in and out more than your chest, or are you still too dependent on those secondary respiratory muscles. In the former case concentrate on slowing and deepening your breathing still further, in the latter change from upside-down to deep diaphragmatic breathing and concentrate on using it for as long as possible. If you miss a trigger or two at first, don't worry. Simply turn the moment you realized you missed it as a reminder to focus on and, where necessary, change your breathing.

After the first week, introduce six more triggers while retaining those you are already using. Continue to do so each week until your new pattern of deep, diaphragmatic breathing is so well-established that it has become automatic and replaced the dysfunctional pattern of inhalation and exhalation you have been following for years.

Method Two: Using a Timer

It is all too easy for very busy people to forget so many trigger points that they rapidly lose motivation and abandon all attempts to change their breathing. Many of my clients prefer to set themselves a clear reminder by using some kind of mechanical or electronic timer.

Suppose you decide, for the first week, to focus on and if necessary alter your pattern of breathing, once an hour throughout the working day. Set the timer so that it warns you when 60 minutes has passed. Then, if possible, stop what you are doing an spend a few moments first paying attention to and then changing how you are breathing.

If already breathing deeply and diaphragmatically, then merely focus on the way each breath is being taken in and, where necessary, slow and deepen each inhalation and exhalation accordingly. Make sure your stomach is expanding freely and fully so that 80 per cent of the movements required for breathing are being performed from the abdomen and only 20 per cent by the secondary respiratory muscles in the ribcage and shoulders.

Should you notice that your chest and shoulders are rising more than your abdomen, however, deliberately switch from diaphragmatic breathing and focus on expanding your stomach as you inhale slowly, deeply and fully. Then pull your abdominal muscles smoothly and gently inwards as you expel the last breath of stale air from deep within your lungs.

If you are unable for any reason to pay attention to your breathing at the moment the timer tells you, then merely reset it to another time – perhaps 15 or 30 minutes ahead – when it will be possible to do so. In any event try to focus on and adjust your breathing a minimum of six times in the first week, twelve times in the second week and eight times in week three. At this point you should be breathing abdominally most if not all of the time.

Remember that this type of breathing is only suitable when in a relaxed state of mind and body. If you have to expend a great deal of physical effort, such as when playing a sport, running for a train or even walking briskly, your body will correctly switch to more costal breathing. Although, as I have explained, this is inappropriate for most of our daily activities, it comes into its own during periods of exertion as it allows the gas exchanges in the lungs to occur more rapidly. In this way the muscles and brain receive the additional oxygen required to metabolize fuel to meet rapid but short-lived increases in energy demand.

Before ending this chapter I should make a few comments on the enemies of high-performance diaphragmatic breathing. There are eight of them and you should be aware of them, and so far as is possible avoid them all.

1. **Sitting or standing in a slumped posture, resting the weight of your body on your arms and shoulders while seated.** When seated ensure your back is upright and well supported with your legs uncrossed. When standing the best pose to adopt is the military 'at ease' position, with your body upright but relaxed and your hands lightly clasped behind your back. Holding your hands in this position will help strengthen and support the spine. Remember that your vertebral column is at its strongest when upright and at its most vulnerable when bent. Check out the difference even a slight angle can make by trying to break a match held either vertically or sloping. In the former case it is very hard to snap, in the second extremely easy.

2. **A ramrod posture.** Boys especially are likely to be told by physical education teachers, parents and adult relatives that they

should stand tall, with a stiffly held spine, shoulders pulled back, chest thrown out and stomach held in. The only consequence of such misguided advice is, of course, a well-established pattern of dysfunctional, upside-down breathing.

3. **Smoking.** This obviously harms you in many different ways as I explained in Chapter Six. So far as breakthrough breathwork is concerned, however, consider only two of them. First your red blood cells, which transport oxygen around the body and have a far greater affinity for carbon monoxide, a major gas in cigarette smoke, than they do for oxygen. This means that when life-giving air has to compete with this potentially lethal gas there really is no contest with death winning out over life every time. Second, smokers have a tendency to use the muscles around their lips to suck air into the lungs even when not smoking, causing them to breathe in a very shallow and inefficient way.

4. **Ties.** Men are often obliged to wear a tie as part of their company's dress code. If you are one of them, then loosen the tie and undo your top collar button as soon as you can and leave them like this for as long as you are able.

5. **Trousers or skirts that hold you tightly around the waist.** Where possible choose loose-fitting designs and clothes made from fabrics which expand. If you are obliged to constrict your waist try to make sure the waistband can be made as loose as possible and can expand as your abdomen expands, for instance after eating a big meal.

6. **Belts.** Make sure your belt is loosely notched and neither too narrow nor so wide that it pinches both your stomach and your diaphragm as you sit down.

7. **High heels that distort your balance, causing your back and hence your breathing muscles to tighten.** Try and wear flat shoes for most of the day even if the need to appear fashionable for important meetings means you have to put on high heels from time to time.

8. **Finally, women should make a point of avoiding girdles, corsets and tightly fitting bras.**

You will find that breaking free from the habit of dysfunctional breathing is a lot less difficult than it may appear and that the rewards for doing so are out of all proportion to the time and effort involved. So make a start today and see how quickly and easily you can enhance every aspect of your life. Once you have established good core stability and made Deep Diaphragmatic Breathing a natural and normal aspect of daily life you will be in an excellent position to master the procedures that follow. These are designed for use in specific situations, ranging from controlling stress and banishing fatigue to improving concentration and removing b-locks to personal development and progress.

CHAPTER THIRTEEN

Procedure Three: the relaxing breath

Live beside a busy highway or railway track and, in a very short space of time, you stop hearing any trains. The same applies to stress. The pace and pressure of modern life is such that we endure so much stress over so long a period that it ceases to be noticed. We live with it, eat, drink and sleep with it and, for most of the time, manage to ignore it's looming presence in our lives. We get so used to disturbed sleep, mild headaches or muscle pains that these soon come to be seen as a natural and normal part of our life — the inevitable price we must pay for being high achievers in a highly competitive world.

We sedate ourselves with alcohol to deaden the pain or stimulate a flagging system with nicotine and caffeine — the latter now being the world's most popular and widely consumed psychoactive drug. In some high-pressure industries, such as advertising and the financial markets, exhausted workers also resort to illegal and far more powerful drugs in order to 'keep on top of things' and make themselves feel good about life.

While there are no sure-fire, certain cures for stress it is a matter of common sense and common observation that, as a Chinese sage remarked, the biggest problems in the world might have been solved quickly and easily when they were still small. That is my own approach to stress management in the real world of work – by this I mean a world in which, however much stressed employees would like to spend an hour each day meditating or relaxing, they rarely have the time to do so. As one executive put it: 'If I had the time to spend an hour relaxing each day I would not need to relax in the first place!'

Fortunately, however, as I pointed out in my book *One-Minute Stress Management* there are a great many things that you can do in less than a minute that will help you unwind mentally and physically. While none of these will eliminate stress, they will give you a much better chance of avoiding the 'last straw' syndrome in which one demand too many, no matter how trivial, can topple you into a stress-related crisis.

The analogy I use for such quick and easy procedures is that of a tumbler filled with water. When topped up right to the very brim it only takes a single additional drop (what we might term the 'final straw') for the liquid to overflow. Reduce the content of the tumbler by half, however, and you have capacity to add a lot more water before disaster occurs.

Of all the many ways of emptying the stress glass none is faster, more effective or more easily mastered than the breakthrough breathing procedure I am now going to describe. Perfect this by practising twice a day for 3 minutes for one week and you will have at your disposal a potent antidote to anxiety, stress and strain in both mind and body.

What the Relaxing Breath Will Do for You

This special type of breathing is designed to help you control and reduce those everyday stresses and pressures of modern life which not only undermine your happiness and well-being but also make it far harder to remain within your O-Zone. This is essential for optimal performance, especially under competitive conditions, since as you will now appreciate, anxiety and stress shift you rapidly to the right of the arousal curve, frequently leading to an abrupt and catastrophic decline in ability. Where the stress and/or anxiety are due to some specific situation, event or circumstances, however, you should also use Procedure Six: Breakthrough Breathing in order to identify and then eliminate the b-lock(s) responsible. Unless this is done you may find yourself merely dealing with the symptoms without ever eliminating the underlying cause.

Recall the case histories I described in Chapters One and Two and you will appreciate that no relaxation procedure, however powerful, would have enabled those clients to remain within their O-Zones. It was only after Jason and Jacquie had identified and eliminated the b-locks responsible for those difficulties that they were able to make progress.

While this procedure is perfect for dealing with stresses and pressures caused by the rough and tumble of daily life it cannot be guaranteed to eliminate permanent problems originating in long-lasting, and perhaps long-forgotten, traumas.

The relaxing breath calms you down and brings any feelings of stress and anxiety in two main ways. First it adjusts the chemistry of the body through ensuring that the acid/alkaline ratio of the blood is maintained at the correct balance. You will recall that the rapid, shallow breathing accompanying many stressful or anxiety-arousing encounters causes more carbon dioxide than usual to be removed from the blood. This, in turn, leads to a significant over-stimulation of the nervous system that intensifies fear and panic as part of our primitive survival mechanism, the fight or flight response.

The second way in which the relaxing breath functions is by producing a specific type of electrical activity in the brain. Studies using a great many individuals, drawn from all ages and walks of life, has shown me that breathing in the way I am about to describe increases the output of both high end Theta (6–8 Hz) and low end Alpha (9–12 Hz) waves while keeping Beta to a minimum. You can find a graph representing this pattern of brain waves in Appendix One. Subjectively, the presence of these frequencies results in a state of calm and relaxed alertness. Ideal conditions in which to use the sensualization I shall describe in a moment.

Let's Make a Start

Find somewhere quiet and private where you can spend the next three minutes alone and undisturbed. Sit in a comfortable chair that offers good support for your spine or lie down on a bed or on the floor. Loosen any tight clothing such as a belt, bra or tie. Uncross your legs and let your arms hang down by your sides. Start by spending a few moments going through the major muscle groups and relaxing away any tensions within them. Allow your shoulders to sag; if your fists are clenched then open them and relax the fingers. Smooth out your brow and rest your head back against the support of the chair, bed or floor. Let your jaw hang loose, tongue resting on the floor of your mouth, lips slightly parted. Take great care to breathe through your nose, not your mouth, throughout the exercise that follows.

When you feel settled and somewhat physically relaxed, take *three* deep, slow, diaphragmatic breaths, as shown in Procedure Two. Make sure the air flows into and away from your body, via the nostrils, in a smooth, effortless, almost fluid movement. Extend your stomach outwards on the inhaled breath and draw it in again to expel the air from deep within your lungs. As you exhale, imagine all the stress and tension flowing away from your body and out into the surrounding room. Without pausing, inhale for around 10 seconds then, again without holding your breath, exhale for the same amount of time.

These three breaths will take around 30 seconds to complete, after which move directly to the second step in this exercise, the relaxing breath itself.

Performing the Relaxing Breath Procedure

Using the thumb and first finger of your left hand apply very light and gentle pressure to the *upper* part of your nose.

Now inhale slowly and deeply for a count of 5 seconds through your partly closed nose. The pressure applied to your nostrils must never be such that inhaling requires any great effort. A very slight constriction is all you require. In the unlikely event that you experience any discomfort, release the pressure immediately and then breathe slowly and calmly through your fully opened nostrils for a few moments before reapplying an even lighter and more gentle pressure to the upper part of the nostrils. Getting the pressure exactly right takes a little experiment and practice but within a couple of practice sessions you should be doing so immediately and easily. Release the pressure on your nostrils as you hold that breath for a further 5 seconds. Partially constrict the nostril again as you exhale slowly and deeply for 8 seconds.

The full sequence of actions is as follows:

1. Partially close the upper part of your nostrils using the thumb and first finger of your left hand.
2. Inhale slowly and deeply while counting to five. The inhaled breath should take around 5 seconds.
3. Release the pressure on your nostrils while keeping your hand in position ready to close them again as you start to exhale.
4. Hold the breath for 5 seconds (a slow count to five is sufficiently accurate).
5. Partially close the nostrils again and exhale for 8 seconds (a slow count to eight is sufficiently accurate).

6. Immediately inhale for 5 seconds and repeat the sequence four more times.

Here is the procedure again, this time with the full cycle to make it easier to follow during the early training.

The Relaxing Breath Cycle

- Inhale through partially closed nostrils (slow count to 5).
- Relax the pressure as you hold your breath (slow count to 5).
- Exhale through partially closed nostrils (slow count to 8).
  Ends cycle one

- Inhale through partially closed nostrils (slow count to 5).
- Relax the pressure as you hold your breath (slow count to 5).
- Exhale through partially closed nostrils (slow count to 8).
  Ends cycle two

- Inhale through partially closed nostrils (slow count to 5).
- Relax the pressure as you hold your breath (slow count to 5).
- Exhale through partially closed nostrils (slow count to 8).
  Ends cycle three

- Inhale through partially closed nostrils (slow count to 5).
- Relax the pressure as you hold your breath (slow count to 5).
- Exhale through partially closed nostrils (slow count to 8).
  Ends cycle four

- Inhale through partially closed nostrils (slow count to 5).
- Relax the pressure as you hold your breath (slow count to 5).
- Exhale through partially closed nostrils (slow count to 8).
  Ends exercise

Breathing in this slow and deliberate way means that the cycle of five relaxing breaths will take around 90 seconds. With the 30 seconds of deep diaphragmatic breathing that preceded the relaxing breath, the total elapsed time for this exercise is now 2 minutes.

Spend the final 60 seconds sensualizing the scene described below. As you do so focus on keeping your breathing slow, deep and effortless. Note, however, that these timings represent the minimum necessary to obtain benefits from this procedure.

You can if you wish extend the exercise by two or three times provided you always extend each time period by the same amount. For instance if you decide to spend *six* minutes on this procedure then use deep diaphragmatic breathing for one minute, the relaxing breath for *three* minutes (do this by doubling the number of cycles, not by extending the periods of inhalation, breath holding and exhalation) and *two* minutes of sensualization.

Before starting this exercise for the first time please take note of the following points:

* In the very unlikely event that you feel light-headed or are in any other way discomforted by the exercise, STOP immediately. Take a short rest and then start again when these feelings have passed.
* The breathwork sequence – inhale 5 seconds, hold 5 seconds and exhale 8 seconds – is the one I train students to follow, since studies that involved simultaneously measuring EEG output and respiration have shown it to produce the desired mental state most easily.
* Initially a few students have difficulty maintaining a full 8 seconds of exhalation. Since all the breathwork procedures taught in this book must always be performed in a relaxed and effortless manner, this is the last thing you want to happen.
* At first, therefore, you can stop exhaling as soon as any difficulties are experienced. Simply note how long you were able to exhale

and, on the next practice session, try to extend this time – even by a single additional second – provided you are able to do so whilst remaining calm and relaxed. After a little practice you should find no difficulty sustaining a smooth and effortless exhalation for the full 8 seconds.

* When exhaling, gently draw in your diaphragm in order to expel the last of the air from deep in your lungs.
* Do not pause between the end of the exhalation and the start of the next inhalation. The only time you hold your breath is after the 5-second inhalation.

As soon as you complete the relaxing breath sequence close your eyes, if you have not already done so, and start working with the sensualization I describe below. I suggest that you follow my script for the first few sessions, always provided of course, that nothing in the imagery causes you to feel anxious. If it does, then devise a similar scenario for yourself, involving a similarly tranquil setting such as a country meadow or sitting snug and warm in your favourite armchair. Try and use all the relevant senses as I described in Chapter Nine. Even if some seem harder to conjure up than others, by persevering you will find the relevant sensations come more and more easily.

While sensualizing keep your breathing slow, regular and effortless using relaxed attention to remain focused on the sounds, sight, smell, taste and touch of the scene before you. Remember that fully developing such sensualizations is not something that can be rushed and that it will take a little while before the sights, sounds, smells and other physical sensations come easily and feel completely natural.

Creating Your Personal Private Paradise

I suggest the majority of students start with this sensualization for the following reasons:

- All the sights and sounds involved are sufficiently familiar for most people to find them easy to conjure up.
- Most of us have spent time by or on the sea, know the relaxing sounds of surf gently breaking on a sandy shore, have tasted the salty tang of the ocean on our lips and smelled the exotic aromas of tropical flowers. Most of us also feel far more relaxed when lying on a warm sandy beach.
- The sound of the sea and its restless but gentle motion when only a soft breeze is blowing combine to produce, in the majority of people, an almost hypnotic state of relaxed tranquillity. This is, of course, an important reason why we find a holiday beside the sea so refreshing.
- Finally, perhaps because we originally came from the sea, and spent the first nine months of our existence bathed in a sea substitute (the amniotic fluid in our mother's womb), there is an almost mythic quality to the oceans. While swimming in warm, crystal clear waters we are no longer subjected to the force of gravity. We live not in the two dimensional world of solid earth but in a world of three dimensional movement where we can fin down into the depths or soar upwards to the sky. For this reason sensualizations involving the oceans are an incredibly powerful aid to mental and physical relaxation.

If however you are made even slightly anxious by the thought of the substitute the scenario I provide below for another – perhaps one based on images of lush green meadows with a crystal clear brook bubbling along over smooth pebbles.

Incidentally if you like the sensualization below but find some of the images and sounds difficult to imagine, then I have produced a 30-minute video incorporating much of what is described below. You can find it on my website at www.BreakthroughBreathwork.com

How to Proceed

After two minutes spent carrying out the breathing exercises described above go through the following sensualization for a further 60 seconds. You can, of course, extend this time period should you wish to do so, but even in a minute you will experience a significant reduction in mental and physical stress.

I suggest that you read through the description below a few times until you get a good idea of the key details of the scenario. At that point you should be able to reconstruct a very similar sensualization in your own imagination. It does not have to be a word for word reproduction of what I have written, but should incorporate the main ideas, which are marked below in bold type.

Alternatively you might wish to tape record the description and play back the cassette during early training sessions. If you do, please speak slowly and clearly. Leave space between the key ideas so that the images, the sounds, the aromas and the bodily sensations can form calmly and unhurriedly in your mind's eye.

Your Personal Private Paradise Sensualization

Imagine that you are swimming through the clear, calm waters of a southern ocean. You can **see** ripples from the surf on the sandy ocean floor beneath and watch as brightly coloured fish dart through beams of sunlight shimmering on the beautiful corals. You can **feel** the warmth of the water as it flows around your body. Your arms and legs are **moving** effortlessly, taking you in any direction you wish to go. One moment you are swimming among the rainbow shoals of fish, the next diving to explore an exquisite reef. You can **feel** your whole body becoming more and more deeply relaxed. You **see** that you are swimming gently and confidently towards a beautiful tropical island that will become your own personal and private paradise – an island of peace and tranquillity amid the storms and tempests of life on which you will feel utterly safe and secure. You can **see** it rising from the azure blue of the ocean. You can **hear** the surf gently uncurling on the brilliantly gold sand of the shore. In the middle distance you can **see** palm tree fronds moving slowly to and fro in the slight and refreshing breeze.

Emerging from the sea you walk along the beach **feeling** the warm sand under your bare feet and **tasting** the salty tang of the air on your lips. You can **see** a line of surf to your right and **hear** the soft and restful splash of the surf as wavelets uncurl themselves idly on the beach. To your left you can also **see** an abundance of gloriously coloured and sweetly scented tropical flowers, their aromas drifting towards you on the balmy air. Around and about the flowers is a flock of bright humming birds, their vivid yellow, blue and red hues standing out against the deep green of the foliage. You can **see** them very clearly as you **hear** their beautiful song.

You stop and lie down on golden sand that **feels** warm and silky smooth beneath your body. Before you lies the crescent of a bay, an arc of golden sand fringed by a line of white surf with the deep blue ocean beyond. A few white, fluffy clouds move slowly across the blue sky above your head. You can **see** all this vividly and in great detail. You can **hear** the gently breaking waves, the rustle of the palms and the song of the birds. You can **smell** the flowers and **taste** the salty tang of the ocean on your lips. You can **feel** the sun warming your body and the warmth of the sand beneath your back and legs.

You are feeling very deeply relaxed. Your mind is calm and completely free from any anxiety or concerns. You know that on your own personal and private paradise island nothing bad can ever come to harm you.

- Here it is possible to relax deeply and in complete security.
- Your muscles **feel** warm and pleasantly heavy.
- There is no tension in your feet, your legs or your abdomen.
- Your breathing is smooth, effortless, deep and slow.
- There is no tension in your hands, arms or shoulders.
- Your face is relaxed, your brow unfurrowed.
- Your lips slightly parted, your tongue is resting loosely in your mouth, your jaw is loose with the upper teeth resting lightly against the lower ones.
- With each, slow intake of breath you are feeling more and more deeply relaxed. Every time you breathe out you feel a little more of the stress and tension flowing away from your body and out into the surrounding room.

Now count backwards from five to one. When you reach one, open your eyes and stand or sit up slowly and continue with your normal routine. As you do so, however, try and carry those feelings of perfect calm and deep relaxation through into your everyday life. Now and again check that you are not holding unnecessary tension anywhere in your body.

- Are your legs uncrossed?
- Are your shoulders hanging loose or held in a needlessly tense posture?
- Is your back upright yet still relaxed?
- Are your hands and wrists relaxed when not being used?
- Is your brow smooth? Are your lips slightly parted?

Regular checks such as this only take a few seconds to complete, yet can spare you needless and easily avoided aches and pains caused by needlessly holding muscles under tension.

Remember too that because your brain is constantly monitoring the tension of all your more than 600 muscles, unnecessary tension in the body can trigger stress reactions in the brain.

Some Points about this Sensualization

* It often happens when you first start practising this type of relaxation that as you begin to unwind you suddenly tense up again. I have seen this occur time and again, as have all psychologists and therapists who teach relaxation.
* The explanation is simple. We are so unfamiliar with what it feels like to be deeply relaxed that some part of our minds regards it as a somewhat abnormal condition to be in, and jerks us out of it again. It is almost as if this part of the brain is saying: 'What on earth are you doing! Don't you know how dangerous the world is? Can't you see how important it is to be constantly alert and vigilant. Come on snap out of it you sentries, wake up and return to duty before some terrible misfortune overwhelms us all!'
* If this happens to you just notice your sudden increase in arousal in a calm and relaxed way, then refocus your inner mind on the relaxing sensualization. In a short space of time you should find these feelings of apprehension disappear entirely as mind and body not only get used to a relaxed state but eagerly welcome it.
* You may also find that intruding thoughts enter your mind. Just as you are trying to focus on the tranquil beach scene, a worry or self-doubt insists on making its unwelcome presence felt. When this happens, and it almost certainly will at first, simply notice the thought casually before refocusing on the sensualization.

- If the intruding thought persists, you might find it helpful to 'write' the worry down in your mind's eye using a stick to mark the words on the damp sand immediately above the surf line – just as you did when a child.

- Now observe the incoming sea washing away those words and, as this happens, allow the same unwanted worry to be washed from your mind.

- Once you have gone through this sensualization a few times you'll find you can use it to good effect even without the relaxing breath, should it prove difficult or embarrassing to go through the whole procedure. Use it while travelling on public transport, for example, or at night should sleep prove elusive, or if you just want to snatch a few minutes to wind down on arriving home. Simply close your eyes and spend some 'me time' in your personal private paradise.

- Return to that very special island any time you start feeling stressed or pressured by life. Even a 60-second holiday will help you feel less tense, more relaxed and better able to face the demands of a busy life.

Try and practise the relaxing breath together with the sensualization twice a day for a week in order to get the sequence of breathwork established and to become more closely acquainted with the island. A good time to do these sessions is around mid-morning, when it will help you remove the stresses and pressures of the first part of the day, and last thing at night. Using the relaxing breath procedure while lying in bed will help you enjoy a more restful and deeply refreshing sleep. You will most probably drift off while still lying in the sun on the beach in your personal private paradise.

CHAPTER 14

Procedure Four: the energizing breath

Imagine this scene. You've just arrived home at the end of a long, hard day and are drained of energy. All you want to do is slump exhaustedly into your favourite armchair and chill out watching some trash TV. It's a natural enough desire. Unfortunately, however, there are still more demands about to be made on your time as you plunge back into the domestic routine, prepare for a night out or get changed for a trip to the health club.

Or picture another scenario, this time at work. You've been putting in long hours preparing an important report that you must present to senior management the following day. As you sit, hour after hour, in front of your computer terminal you can feel your eyelids growing heavy with fatigue. It is getting harder and harder to focus on the key messages or even to get your words down in a meaningful order. Yet there is no time to take a break or have a rest. The hands on the clock above your desk are relentlessly ticking towards the onrushing deadline. It's just a question of who is going to get there first, your final report or your complete exhaustion.

In our time-pressured culture, where we often have 268 or more hours of demands to somehow squeeze into the 168 hours available to us each week, mental fatigue is rapidly becoming the number one threat to both personal success and physical health.

I am often reminded, when talking to some of my corporate clients, of these wonderful lines from A.A. Milne, creator of Winnie the Pooh: 'Here is Edward Bear coming down the stairs now, bump, bump, bumping his head behind Christopher Robin. It is, so far as he is aware, the only way of coming down the stairs. Although he sometimes considers there must be a better way if only he could stop bumping his head long enough to think of it!'

Well, fortunately there *is* a better way and one that you can fit into the few minutes available to you between stopping one activity and starting on another. It's called the energizing breath and, as the name suggests, you will use it to increase your level of mental and physical vitality any time you feel fatigue moving you to the left of your O-Zone.

Unlike all but one other Breakthrough Breathwork procedures I have developed over the years – which is deep diaphragmatic breathing – this powerful technique has been around for centuries. Those of you who have studied yoga will instantly recognize it as Sun-Moon or Alternate Nostril Breathing. I am including it here because in laboratory studies of the relationship between breathing and brain waves I have found it to be highly effective in creating the ideal mental state for restoring flagging energy to mind and body.

As you can see from the graph in the Appendix (2) this ancient breathwork procedure significantly increases Alpha (the brain wave associated with a state of relaxed alertness) while at the same time reducing Theta (early-stage sleep waves) and allowing Beta (high-activity waves) to remain reasonably high. My research suggests that this pattern of brain waves is associated with subjective feelings of a relaxed, but alert and energized, mental and physical state.

You can also use the same approach to:

* Soothe and calm frayed nerves.
* Increase levels of alertness.

- Focus and concentrate your mind.
- In any situation where levels of mental and/or physical arousal are starting to move you beyond the O-Zone of maximum performance.

Before explaining how you do it – and the movements involved are simplicity itself – let's carry out a simple experiment that will give you an insight into a little known aspect of breathing.

Your Erectile Nose!

Gently close your right nostril and inhale a few times through the left. Now close your left nostril and repeat, this time inhaling through the right. You will almost certainly find the air flows more easily and smoothly through one nostril than the other. If you repeat the exercise in around 90 minutes' time, however, you should find that the air now flows more freely through the alternate nostril. This is because, lying beneath the mucus membrane, is a thick, spongy tissue layer that rapidly fills with blood. It is a specialized type of tissue also found in the breasts and genitals that makes possible the erection of the penis and clitoris during sexual arousal. As a result, there is an intimate relationship between sexual activity and blocked-up nostrils – a medical condition known to doctors as 'honeymoon nose'!

Within the nose, the engorgement of this tissue with blood follows a clear pattern called an ultradian rhythm with a cycle of about 90 minutes, which explains why it is easier to breathe through one nostril than the other at different times of the day. Opinion is divided over the exact purpose of these rhythmic changes within the nasal cavity. One view is that when we are using right nostril breathing the left hemisphere of our brain receives greater stimulation than the left. Once the switch over has occurred and left nostril breathing predominates the right hemisphere receives more stimulation. This natural rhythm ensures both hemispheres are equally stimulated over a 24-hour period.

Certainly the Yogis who have devoted their lives to the study and practice of breathing believe it brings about profound psychological consequences. They claim, for example, that right nostril breathing is associated with more outwardly directed and aggressive behaviour whilst left nostril dominance produces a more passive and contemplative state of mind.

By using the energizing breath, also known as *nadi shodhanam* or alternate nostril breathing, therefore, you will help restore harmony and balance to your mind and body. Indeed, so life- and energy-enhancing is this simple and straightforward procedure that that some of my clients refer to it as their '3-minute miracle'.

Let's Begin

Start by forming a triangle with the thumb, first and middle finger of your *right* hand. Rest your thumb lightly against your *right* nostril and place your middle finger against your *left* nostril. Your first finger rests on the centre of your forehead directly above the top of your nose to provide support for the thumb and middle finger, as shown on the next page.

Next, using your thumb, completely close your *right* nostril and inhale as slowly, smoothly and as deeply through your *left* nostril for 5 seconds.

Now, without holding your breath, immediately breathe out through the *left* nostril, for 10 seconds. If you cannot, initially, exhale for that length of time without straining then maintain the out breath for as long as you can comfortably manage to do so. Use the diaphragm to expel the last of the air from your lungs, but be careful to remain comfortable and relaxed.

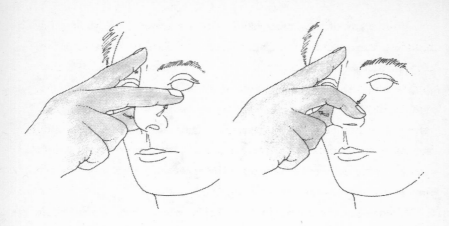

Without pausing, or holding your breath, release the *right* nostril by lifting your thumb and shut off the *left* one by applying gentle but firm pressure from your middle finger. Inhale for 5 seconds through your *right* nostril.

At the end of this time, once again without pausing or holding your breath, close your *right* nostril and exhale for 10 seconds (or as near to this as you can comfortably manage) through your *left* nostril.

As before, without pausing or holding your breath, close your *left* nostril and inhale through the right.

Each cycle of inhalation and exhalation, if carried out as suggested above, will take 15 seconds. That is 5 seconds to inhale and 10 seconds to exhale then 5 seconds to inhale once again. In the first two minutes, therefore, you will be able to complete eight complete cycles.

If you wish – and have the time – you can of course continue using the energizing breath for a longer period. Some breathing specialists suggest that 20 cycles are most appropriate. In my work with pressured executives, however, I usually find that three minutes is the upper limit of the time they can practically and comfortably devote to any single exercise. After that they either get interrupted by a phone call or visitor or else their mind starts wandering and they lose focus.

While I am, of course, an enthusiastic proponent of anything that reduces stress, enhances individual well-being and improves performance, I also recognize that in the modern world such interventions must be practically possible. In my view, therefore, performing any exercise or procedure with care, attention and excellent technique for 3 minutes is better than spending twice as long but losing focus and allowing technique to deteriorate. In all forms of exercise what is needed to produce consistently good results is the quality not the quantity of application.

When using the energizing breath procedure bear in mind these two important points.

1. Only change nostrils (closing one and opening the other) after an exhaled breath. This is why, at the start, I asked you to inhale and then exhale through the left nostril prior to changing over.
2. Never hold your breath between inhalation and exhalations. The air must be allowed to flow smoothly into and out of your body via each nostril in turn.

Here's a summary of the energizing breathing cycle. Although it may appear slightly complicated at first, after a couple of trial runs you should find it quick and easy to use.

1. Rest your thumb lightly against your right nostril and place your middle finger against your left nostril.
2. Rest your first finger against the centre of your forehead directly above the top of your nose to provide support.
3. Using your thumb, completely close your right nostril and inhale as slowly, smoothly and as deeply as you can through your left nostril for FIVE seconds (a slow count to five is sufficiently accurate for this purpose).

4. Without pausing or holding your breath, immediately breathe out through your left nostril for TEN seconds. Once again you can use a slow count to ten to measure this time.

5. If unable comfortably to exhale for 10 seconds continue doing so for as long as you feel easily able and build up to this time over a period.

6. Without pausing or holding your breath, release the right nostril and close the left one using your middle finger.

7. Inhale for FIVE seconds through your right nostril.

8. Once again, without pausing or holding your breath, release the left nostril and close the right one using your middle finger.

9. Exhale through your left nostril for TEN seconds then change nostrils and inhale through the right side for FIVE seconds.

10. Repeat each cycle eight times, remembering you ONLY change nostrils after an exhalation and NEVER pause or hold your breath between each inhalation and exhalation. The air must flow smoothly into and out of the body.

11. With each cycle of inhalation and exhalation lasting around 15 seconds, eight repetitions will occupy the first 2 minutes of your 3-minute session.

At the end of 2 minutes, switch to deep diaphragmatic breathing as you work with the sensualization described below.

The Energizing Breath Sensualization

Having prepared yourself mentally using two minutes of energizing breathing and then switched to deep diaphragmatic breathing you should use the following sensualization. For your first few sessions, I suggest that you stick fairly precisely to the description below, modifying or changing it to suit your particular personal needs as you gain experience with the procedure. If, however, you would prefer not to use the island setting I am using in all the sensualizations described in this book, but prefer instead to work with the scenario developed in the previous procedure, feel free to do so here as well. Simply modify that sensualization to include the key elements described below.

Close your eyes and return to the personal private paradise island you created for the relaxing breath procedure. **See** yourself lying on golden beach, **feel** the sun warm on your body and the soft sand beneath your feet, **hear** the gently breaking surf and **smell** the rich scent of the tropical flowers. Now imagine yourself walking down a wide, flower-fringed path through a broad avenue of trees. **Notice** how the muscles in your legs are **moving** as you proceed slowly and calmly through the clearing. **See** the dancing interplay of sunlight and shadows, **feel** the light breeze on your skin, **hear** the gentle rustle of the leaves and the birdsong and **smell** the sweet aroma of the flowers.

In a clearing you find a crystal clear waterfall flowing down the side of a rocky scarp and into a small stream. **Hear** the sound of the water as it tumbles into the stream. **Notice** how the sparkling droplets catch the beams of sunlight shafting through the trees. **See** the bubbles of air and eddies as the water swirls into the basin directly beneath the waterfall. **Feel** the cooling spray against your face and body as you step closer, stoop to cup your hands beneath the waterfall, collect some of the pure, clear water and raise it to your lips. **Notice** the coolness of the water as it tumbles into your cupped hands and the soft coldness as it enters your mouth and travels down your throat.

Now, as you swallow a handful of this water, a remarkable transformation takes place in your mind and body. It is as though the energy of the sunlight itself is entering you, starting at the top of your head and cascading, like the water, through your entire being. This beam of golden white liquid light is flowing from your crown and down your spine, around your shoulders, along your arms and through your hands until it is pouring from your fingertips in ten brilliant shafts of spreading illumination. It fills your chest, enters your abdomen and floods down your legs, ankles and feet until the beams of light are also shooting from each of your ten toes.

You have been filled by pure energy that pours forth in abundance from your nostrils and ears, your eyes and mouth, your fingers, your navel and the tips of your toes, spreading and diffusing until you are totally surrounded by a golden halo of energy. **Feel** it revitalize every cell in your body, driving away the darkness of fatigue and replacing it with the power and potency of sunlight. Focus on these pleasant, the energizing sensations for the remainder of your 60-second sensualization.

At the end of this time count slowly backwards from five to one and open your eyes, returning to the world re-energized and revitalized to continue with your daily tasks, all traces of fatigue banished from your mind and body

This concludes the energizing breath procedure.

CHAPTER FIFTEEN

Procedure Five: the focused breath

Many of us spend far less time in the present than we do in either the past or future. We dream about what might or will happen. We reflect fondly or unhappily on what has happened. We reflect on or anticipate events far more frequently and intensely than we ever focus on the here and now. As a result, concentrating on any one idea or external object for more than a few moments becomes virtually impossible. No matter how hard we try unwanted distractions intrude on our thoughts. When people first start to meditate, for example, they find their tranquillity invaded by a host of distracting notions and concerns. Their mind drifts aimlessly in time, wandering back and forth in reminiscence or anticipation. We become a prey to worries and concerns which, circling like vultures above a wagon train, become ever harder to ignore. Only after much practice, persistence and concentration does it become possible to still these frenetic thoughts and focus intently on just one aspect of our being, whether the rise and fall of our breath or some external object such as a candle.

At work or at play an ability to focus intently on the here and now is usually essential for achievement. A momentary lapse of concentration when playing a sport or making a business presentation, for example, can turn success into failure. A similar lapse when driving a car or operating other high-speed machinery is liable to have even more catastrophic consequences. Fatigue, worries and problems can all serve to distract our mind from the task at hand and make it harder to concentrate intently on any single activity.

Once we have learned to focus, however, the mind will enter a state that psychologists term 'flow'. In this altered state of consciousness it becomes possible to concentrate so hard on a single chain of thoughts or actions that time itself ceases to have any meaning. Glance at your watch before and immediately after entering a state of flow and you are likely to be amazed at just how much time has flown past. What seemed like no more than a few moments between starting and completing the task may well turn out to have extended for an hour or longer. While in a state of flow your entire being is intently focused on just that single activity. Other sights and sounds are either not noticed, or perceived merely as an unimportant part of the background.

I remember talking to golfer Nick Faldo about the state of flow and absolute focus that all top sportsmen and women, no matter what their game, must possess in order to reach the top. I asked him about an occasion when he was playing at St Andrews, when a gorse fire blew smoke across the course and partly obscured it. 'Were you distracted by the fire?' I enquired. He stared at me uncomprehendingly. 'What fire?' he demanded. So intense had been his concentration and so perfect his focus that he had failed even to notice it.

The following breathwork procedure is designed to help focus your mind more intently on whatever task your are undertaking. As before, it takes 3 minutes to carry out and the effects can last up to an hour or more.

Effect of the Focused Breath

The overall effect of this pattern of breathing is significantly to increase the output of both higher spectrum Theta (4–8 Hz) and Alpha waves

(8–12 Hz) while decreasing high frequency Beta brain waves. You will find a graph showing a typical focused breath brain wave spectrum in the Appendix (3). Subjectively the state of mind that results from this form of breathwork is one of relaxed alertness.

Breathwork for Focused Breathing

Prior to an event where you will need to employ all your powers of concentration in order to succeed, spend 3 minutes on the following procedure.

As I explained in Chapter Six we normally breathe around 17 times a minute, which means that every cycle of inhalation and exhalation lasts between 3 and 4 seconds. To produce the focused breath one needs to slow this rate down to just four a minute, increasing the time of each inhalation to 5 seconds and each exhalation to 10 seconds. When doing so there is no pause between an inhalation and exhalation; the air must flow smoothly into and away from the body.

Let's Begin

1. Sit comfortably with your back straight and spine well supported. You should be able to look straight ahead with your throat fully opened so that the air can pass easily and smoothly down your windpipe and into your lungs. Keep your shoulders dropped and relaxed. Loosen any tight clothing around your neck or stomach. Make sure your head is relaxed and not slumped forward, so constricting the throat.
2. Close your eyes and breathe in deeply and slowly through your nostrils for FIVE seconds (a slow count to five is sufficiently accurate).
3. Allow your stomach to expand outwards as you draw the air deep into your lungs by means of the diaphragm. Imagine there is a

beach ball inside your stomach and that you are filling it with each inhalation.

4. Now, without pausing, exhale slowly for a slow count to TEN once again using the diaphragm to expel as much air as possible from your lungs. If this proves too difficult at first then exhale for as long as is comfortably possible and build slowly to this maximum during your week of training.

5. Repeating this simple cycle eight times will occupy the first 2 minutes of your 3 minutes' focused breath session. In the remaining 60 seconds, use the sensualization below.
    Once again, then, the procedure is:

1. Inhale smoothly and very deeply for a slow count to five.
2. Exhale fully for a count to ten.
3. After eight repetitions move to the sensualization below. While doing so keep your breathing slow and deep.

First Sensualization for Focused Breathing

As before I shall be using the 'island' scenario and suggest that, unless uncomfortable with this approach, you follow it for the first few sessions before modifying or changing it to better suit your personal needs. Equally if you have been working with a different setting then stay with that and change it in line with the description below.

Having spent 2 minutes on focused breathing, return in your mind's eye to your personal private paradise and imagine yourself walking along the golden sands of the foreshore.

To your right you can **see** the perfect blueness of the ocean with small waves breaking on the beach. You can **hear** the rhythmic sounds as they gently uncurl and **feel** the warm sand beneath your feet. You can **taste** the salty tang of the sea air on your lips and **smell** the tropical flowers fringing the beach to your left.

Now I want you to imagine yourself stooping to pick up a beautiful shell from the beach. **Feel** the weight of it in your hand. **Trace** your fingers along its rough outer contours and compare these with the smoothness of the texture inside the shell itself. **Notice** how the sunlight reflects from the polished sheen inside the shell's mouth and imagine what colour this might be, pink fading to white perhaps, or a light blue throughout.

Study this shell as closely and intensely as possible, moving your gaze over the outer regions and noticing how small barnacles have attached themselves to its rough exterior. **Sniff** the shell and absorb the salty aromas of the ocean.

Place it against your ear and **hear** the rushing ebb and flow of the tide echoing from within.

Try and hold these sensations as clearly and accurately as possible for the remainder of the 60 seconds.

On subsequent occasions you may wish to examine some other small aspect of your island paradise in greater detail, perhaps a tropical flower, a piece of sea-weathered timber, the twisted roots of a tree or a piece of gemstone found lying in the sand.

The purpose of this sensualization is to help develop focus and concentration. You will be able to acquire this skill even faster by spending a little time studying actual objects in everyday life. To do this spend 60 seconds or so using focused breathing to establish the desired pattern of brain waves. Then closely observe some small object, such as a fruit, a stone, a piece of weathered timber or a small art object. Concentrate on it in the most minute detail, feel the texture and temperature of the object beneath your fingertips and, where appropriate, pay attention also to the taste, the smell, or any of the sounds associated with it.

Second Sensualization for Focused Breathing

During your second session of the day, sensualize an actual situation, whether in the past or yet to come, in which you will have to remain very strongly focused to achieve your goal. Spend 2 minutes developing the required pattern of brain waves using focused breathing. Then close your eyes and enter that specific situation. **See** yourself being able to focus 100 per cent on the task at hand, without ever allowing unwanted thoughts or external distractions to break your concentration.

If at any time you start to feel your focus slipping, gently but firmly return yourself to the task at hand. Within a very short while you should find it possible to focus intently and for longer and longer periods on any activity that requires your complete concentration in order to achieve your goal.

This concludes Procedure Five on focused breathing.

CHAPTER SIXTEEN

Procedure Six: breakthrough breathing

The purpose of this breakthrough breathing procedure is to bring about a pattern of brain activity in which your mind becomes highly receptive to the removal of those b-locks that are preventing you from remaining within your O-Zone. As we saw in Chapters One and Two this usually happens when rising mental and/or physical arousal start shifting you to the right of the performance curve.

In order to eliminate b-locks it is necessary to produce a mental state that is alert yet reasonably relaxed. This can be achieved by ensuring the presence of high frequency Beta waves (14 Hz and upward) whilst at the same time having substantial levels of both Alpha (8 Hz–14 Hz) and Theta (4 Hz–8 Hz) waves. You will find a graph showing the overall pattern desired in Appendix One.

Removing a b-lock, especially one laid down years, perhaps even decades, earlier and quite probably lying below the level of normal awareness, is never easy or simple. It is however usually possible, and as it can transform almost every aspect of your life it is well worth the time and effort required. If you feel that such a b-lock is holding you back by limiting your ability to think, feel and act as you wish then I do urge you to give this procedure a fair trial. While I cannot guarantee the 100 per cent removal of a deeply rooted b-lock, I can say with fair confidence than the process of identifying and then working towards its elimination will prove both insightful and of considerable therapeutic benefit.

I do urge you, however, to be gentle with yourself and never see the task ahead as some kind of a battle between your conscious and unconscious mind. The process is not about conflict and confrontation any more than the outcome should be judged in terms of success or failure. Simply work calmly and objectively towards the liberation of the person you want to be and rationally know that you can become. Build on insights you achieve along the way and use them to further strengthen your purpose of mind and expand your self-knowledge. Above the oracle at Delphi was the simple but profound command: 'Know Thyself'.

By seeing Breakthrough Breathwork in the light of self-knowledge, rather than as a 'quick fix' for some chronic b-lock, you will gain far more than you might have hoped or expected when starting out on this voyage of personal discovery.

The Three Stages of Eliminating a B-lock

The first stage is, of course, to identify the cause of the problem. As we saw in the first two chapters with the case of Jason, the childhood fire raiser, this can take time and patience. Once you have identified, or believe you have identified, the reason why a b-lock formed then you can move to stage two, which involves using the special pattern of breathing described below to establish the required pattern of brain waves. Finally you will use two forms of sensualization and a particular physical action to dissolve the obstructing b-lock and consign it to the dustbin of your personal history.

Stage One: Identifying the B-lock

It may be that you already know, or think you know, what has led to your current difficulties in certain situations or when confronted by particular challenges.

One woman I helped overcome sexual anxieties vividly recalled how at the age of twelve, while living in France, she had been walking alone in a forest near her home when a man first exposed himself to her and then chased her through the trees. Although he never caught up with her that memory made it impossible for the woman to have enjoyable sex with her partner, even though she loved him very deeply. Each time he made a sexual approach, that dark image rose up in her mind causing her to become frigid. Although she allowed him to make love to her, and although he was tender, sensitive and understanding, the sex act was never more than a distasteful duty for her and, one imagines, an unsatisfactory experience for him.

If you already know, or strongly suspect you know, why a particular b-lock exists then you can move directly to the second step in this process. If it turns out you are not entirely correct in this identification and find that traces of the b-lock still remain at the end of the treatment sessions, simply return to this stage and use the procedures below.

Identifying a B-lock

Proceed as follows. Start by using the relaxing breath (Procedure Three) to bring your mind and body into a state of relaxed alertness. Next enter your own personal private paradise to become even more mentally relaxed. **See** the calm blueness of the ocean and the little waves breaking on the beach. **Hear** the rhythmic sounds as they gently uncurl and **feel** the warm sand beneath your feet. **Taste** the salty tang of the sea air on your lips, as you **smell** the scents of tropical flowers.

Imagine now that, walking along the beach, you come across a small, steeply sided bay. Set into the cliff face are three doors, one to your right, a second to your left and a third, directly ahead and above you reached by a short flight of stone steps cut into the rock. You will probably recognize this sensualization as a modified version of the one I used with Jason and my other clients. I have removed the tunnel element to enable it to be used comfortably and easily by all my readers, even those who may suffer from claustrophobia. If you do have this difficulty then be assured that you will not be asked to think yourself inside small or confined spaces in the sensualization that follows.

Visualize these doors in any way you wish. You may choose to see them as carved from solid timbers and bound with iron, or perhaps they are smoothly sliding modern doors, or transparent glass doors such as you might find opening onto a patio. You make the choice of how they appear, the sounds they make as you open one of them and the feel of the handle under your fingers.

Select any one of the three doors to open while keeping this thought in mind. The door on your left represents a portal opening onto the left side – the mainly logical and analytical hemisphere of your brain. The door on your right represents an entry into the right side – the more intuitive and imaginative hemisphere of your brain. The door directly ahead represents an opening into your higher consciousness.

In the chamber that lies beyond this door you can, if you wish, meet anyone you feel might guide you to the answer you seek. These may be living people whom you might feel embarrassed or uncomfortable about questioning in real life. Equally they can be those you have loved and lost. You may also talk to famous characters from history, from fiction or from religion. Angels, saints or sinners – the choice is yours and limited only by your powers of imagination.

Let us suppose you decide to open the door on your left.

Incidentally never attempt to analyse or rationalize your reasons for making this choice. Nor should you reflect or deliberate prior to choosing. Rather it is important to follow your gut instinct since this is most directly linked to the limbic system, the region of your brain most likely to contain the answers being sought. Trust yourself to *know* at a very deep level, which of the three doors will lead you most swiftly, directly and easily to the truth.

Opening, for the sake of this example, the left door you find yourself standing in a large room. This can be of any size or shape you desire, furnished and decorated in any way that you wish. Walk around it in your sensualization. Examine all the details unfolding before you. Sense the atmosphere. Is the air warm or cold, damp or dry, against your skin? Do your footsteps echo around a stone flagged chamber or does a deep pile carpet muffle them? Is the room brightly lit or full of gloomy shadows? Are the furnishings modern or ancient? What are the ornaments like? Are there pictures on the walls and, if so, what do they depict and in what style are they painted? Are they old masters or modern abstracts? Are there any toys in the room? If so, what type? A train set or a rocking chair, a delicate china doll or a tattered teddy bear?

Spend as much time as you wish in this chamber and make any changes you wish to the design, the décor, the lighting or the furnishings. If it is dark do you want to make it lighter? If it is already very light would you sooner lower the level of illumination? Would you replace antique furnishings and old masters with modern designs and pictures? Once you have made any desired changes leave the room, return to the beach and spend a final few moments relaxing and unwinding before returning to the real world.

You will, of course, follow exactly the same procedure if entering through the right hand door. Here too you will take notice of the décor and furnishings before making any changes to transform that room into somewhere more to your liking.

Entering the Centre Door

If entering the centre chamber imagine it being filled with brilliant white light but possessing no other details. From this light will emerge whomever you summon to aid you in your quest for the truth. Once they have appeared in your imagination, allow intuition to determine the questions you want to put to them and do not in any way attempt to direct or control their replies. If they choose to remain silent, as they may well do on your first few visits, then accept that. Ask them a different question and see whether this elicits a response. If it does then well and good, if not then move to another question.

Never try to work out in advance what questions you want to ask. You'll find they spring to mind without effort once you are in that situation. You may also find that rather than answering in words your responses will be dealt with through a series of images, just as might occur in a dream. Often these images may appear bizarre, having little or no connection with the question you have raised. Never challenge or question these responses at the time. Merely make a mental note of them for future reference.

Once you have made any desired changes leave the room, return to the beach and spend a final few moments relaxing and unwinding before returning to the real world.

Spend the time until to your next sensualization reflecting on what happened in the chambers. Try to relate the objects you found, the ways in which you chose to alter the décor and furnishings, the person you chose to talk to, and the questions you were prompted to ask, to your current difficulties. This is an entirely personal and subjective process, just as is dream interpretation. Because of this I cannot give you a clear lead as to what a certain object, for example, might mean.

Clients often pose questions such as: 'I clearly saw a rocking horse in the right hand chamber. I even climbed on its back and took a ride. Does this mean my b-lock relates to an event in childhood? Perhaps something that happened in my nursery?' Or they may say: 'I spoke to my father who died five years ago. I asked why he always seemed so angry with me. He said nothing but pointed to a beautifully kept garden. He was always a fanatical gardener and it occurred to me he may have blamed me for playing in the garden and perhaps damaging the flowers, although I have no recollection of ever having done so.'

All I can ever say to such queries is – does that seem like a plausible interpretation to you? Does it feel right? Does in fit in with any of the other images that came into your mind at the time or with any of your subsequent recollections? I repeat – there are *no* hard and fast rules.

There are no lists of symbolic meanings for the objects and images your limbic system projects into your conscious mind, as people sometimes attempt – in my view quite mistakenly – to produce for dream analysis. They simply are what they are and any interpretation you place on them is just as likely to be valid as any other.

What tends to happen is that a clear idea about the nature and cause of the b-lock will emerge not at the first or second sensualization but slowly and gradually over a period of time. Persist, however, and the moment will come when the truth emerges and a clear insight occurs. At this point you are ready to move on to Stage Two and learn the breathwork technique needed to eliminate that b-lock once and for all.

Before leaving the first stage of the procedure, let me reassure you that there is nothing spooky or irreligious in what I am describing. I mention this because people are sometimes concerned at what I am asking them to do, especially when it comes to talking with those who are deceased. There is no 'ghost in the machine' and you are not evoking spirits from another world or opening the gates for some kind of demonic possession. All that is happening in each of the three scenarios is that your conscious mind is making direct contact with the limbic regions of your brain. Everything you see or hear, taste, touch or smell arises from within the skull. You are not being put in touch with any external and potentially harmful outside agencies.

All the answers you obtain come not from another world or different dimension but solely from the interior of your own brain – albeit from a region that is not accessible to the conscious mind. This region, for the technical reasons I gave in Chapters Four and Five, is far richer in memories and emotional information than the higher regions of thought ever can be. This is because the bandwidth of consciousness is infinitesimally narrow in comparison with the total bandwidth of the unconscious mind. As a result of this only a very small amount of the total potentially available information stored in memory can be accessed at any one time, and much of it can never, normally, be accessed at all. Most of the time these memories operate below our level of conscious awareness, causing us to think or feel and to act in ways we cannot really understand or easily explain. If consciousness only knew half of what the unconscious mind really knows then we would possess twice the insight into our own true nature and motivations. A good analogy is with lucid dreams. These, as I explained in an earlier chapter, are dreams in which you know you are dreaming and can, at least to some extent, direct the course of the dream. The difference is that here, although in an altered state of mind from that with which you deal with the real world, you remain very much in control of every aspect of the sensualization.

Stage Two: Breakthrough Breathwork

The pattern of breathing you use for developing the required mental state is the most complex of all the procedures described. It involves gradually increasing the amount of time taken when inhaling and exhaling from 2 to 8 seconds and then back down the timing ladder again. There is no need to use a watch or other timer to count the seconds, merely count in your head as you have done previously. After a couple of sessions you will automatically adopt the time intervals required.

The pattern of breathing you will adopt here forms what I term a breathing pyramid that approximates to the shape of the lungs. Start by drawing air into the upper lobes and finish the first sequence by drawing it deep into the lowest areas of the lungs. After that move back up the pyramid again before starting back down once more.

Let's Begin

1. Sit comfortably with your legs uncrossed and your back straight to allow an easy flow of air into the lungs. Loosen any tight clothing around your neck or waist.

2. Start by moving down the breathing pyramid (see page 202) by breathing as follows, making certain not to hold your breath between each inhalation and exhalation.

3. Inhale deeply for slow count to TWO – exhale deeply for slow count to TWO.

4. Inhale deeply for slow count to FOUR – exhale deeply for slow count to FOUR.

5. Inhale deeply for slow count to SIX – exhale deeply for slow count to SIX.

6. Inhale deeply for slow count to EIGHT – exhale deeply for slow count to EIGHT.

7. Now move back up the breathing pyramid and, as before, take care not to hold your breath between each inhalation and exhalation.

8. Inhale deeply for slow count to EIGHT – exhale deeply for slow count to EIGHT.

9. Inhale deeply for slow count to SIX – exhale deeply for slow count to SIX.

10. Inhale deeply for slow count to FOUR – exhale deeply for slow count to FOUR.

11. Inhale deeply for slow count to TWO – exhale deeply for slow count to TWO.

These two cycles will occupy around 40 seconds. Repeat three times more bringing the total to around 160 seconds. Use the final 20 seconds to restore your breathing to a normal pattern of slow, deep, equally spaced inhalations and exhalations.

The illustration below shows you how the Breakthrough Breathing procedure moves you first down and then back up the breathing pyramid.

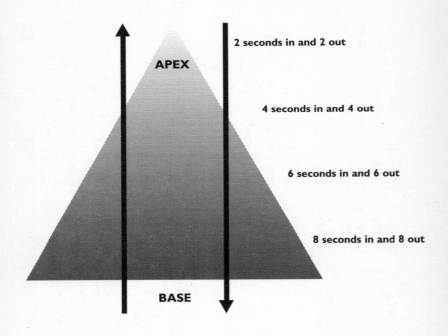

APEX

2 seconds in and 2 out

4 seconds in and 4 out

6 seconds in and 6 out

8 seconds in and 8 out

BASE

Stage Three: Breaking your B-lock

Before proceeding with this stage make sure you have identified, with reasonable certainty, the reason why you became breath locked in the first instance. You should also have practised the pattern of breathing described above on at least six occasions so that it comes easily and naturally. When you are ready to do so proceed as follows:

1. Sitting comfortably with your back straight and your legs uncrossed, use TWO cycles of Breakthrough Breathwork.
2. Immediately after restoring a normal pattern of breathing, bend the fingers of your right and left hands as shown and clasp them together.

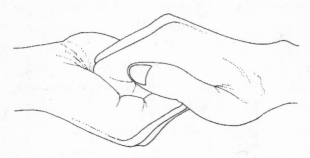

3. Now shut your eyes and sensualize, as vividly and as powerfully as you can that occasion, however many years ago, when the b-lock originated.
4. Remember to see, to hear, to touch and – where appropriate – to taste and smell the event from your own viewpoint.
5. You must never allow yourself to become a detached observer watching events unfold from a distance, or as if on a cinema or TV screen. For the procedure to work it is essential that whatever happens, happens to you in the sensualization just as it did in real life.
6. Be careful here. Sometimes the uncovering and reliving of these traumatic memories is so painful and distressing you will simply not want to go on. If this happens then STOP immediately. Switch instantly to your private personal paradise sensualization and use the relaxing breath procedure to banish any anxieties.
7. Only when you feel able should you attempt to return to the emotionally traumatic sensualization. This might happen after a short period of relaxation; it might not happen until the next session or even for several sessions.

8. If you are able to persevere, however, the time will come when, although it may still cause you mild distress, the pain will subside and you will be able to move forwards without significant discomfort. What you should not do is stop for good and walk away, since a possible consequence is to reinforce the b-lock even more firmly.

9. If you feel, for any reason, that you are not going to be able to face what awaits you in the sensualization then do not proceed further. There is nothing to feel ashamed of in coming to such a decision. Far from being a cowardly response it is actually an extremely sane and sensible one. There really are some traumas that are so terrible, so painful and so overwhelmingly devastating that your conscious mind has banished them forever.

Should this happen to you then there are two possible ways forward. First simply use the relaxation and other procedures I have described to control the symptoms produced by the b-lock without making any attempt to remove it. While not ideal this will make it much easier for you to move forward with your life and make progress towards becoming all you want to become. The second option is to seek professional advice from a training clinical psychologist or therapist. In the secure environment of a one-to-one therapeutic setting with a skilled professional at hand to guide, advise and direct your progress you will be able safely to venture into areas of thought and feelings that could prove dangerous when attempted alone.

I cannot emphasize too strongly that this is an extremely powerful psychological procedure and one that should be taken seriously and only employed after considerable thought and with appropriate care. Assuming you decide to proceed, begin your sensualization a few moments before the events occurred. Step back in time to a moment 5 or 10 minutes before the trauma arose. In the case of Jason, for example, the point of re-entry into his childhood occurred when he scrambled through the bales of straw with a matchbox clutched in his stubby, 5-year-old fingers. It continued as he struck the match and found his secret hiding place abruptly and brilliantly illuminated by a flickering orange yellow light. The next instant a dangling wisp of straw ignites, flares up and suddenly Jason's secret hideaway barn is full of smoke and flames. He can smell and taste the acrid smoke, feel the heat of the blaze and the pain from his grazed knees as he struggles desperately to flee down the narrow passageway between the rapidly igniting bales of straw.

10. Try to develop the same vivid sensualization for your own traumatic event. See it, hear it, feel it, touch and taste it just as you did on the occasion it actually happened.

11. At some point a climax will be reached when you will feel with almost the same physical and mental intensity exactly the same responses as were originally experienced during the event.

12. When this moment occurs start tugging your inter-linked fingers in an effort to break them apart while simultaneously resisting that attempt.

13. Transfer the tension building within the muscles of your fingers, hands, wrists and arms to your fingers. Then, at the moment your emotional tensions climax, allow them to snap apart.

14. Make this action rapid and vigorous, physically symbolizing the fact that the b-lock has been smashed forever, that it will never again be allowed to block or inhibit your progress through life.

15. Feel all the physical tension now draining swiftly away from the muscles in your fingers, hands, wrists and arms as the muscles rebound and relax and allow the emotional stress that has built up during the sensualization similarly to drain away.

In Jason's case that moment of separation came as he sensualized himself opening his eyes and seeing, through a blur of smoke and tears, his father's white and terrified features above

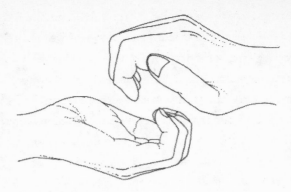

him. At this moment his fingers snapped apart and the b-lock vanished from his life forever.

16. Do not expect that this will always occur instantly. While even a deeply rooted b-lock is sometimes banished forever after a single breakthrough sensualization, more usually many visits to the traumatic epicentre of your problem will be needed in order to remove it fully and permanently.

17. To check whether or not you have finally broken free from the malignant influence of a specific b-lock there is one further step to take. Create another sensualization in which you see, hear, and in every other way see yourself facing up to a challenge that currently causes you difficulties. Once again be sure to do so from your own viewpoint. You might wish to choose an actual event and replay it in your mind's eye to see whether on this occasion you can perform as you would ideally liked to have performed at the time. Or you can anticipate an upcoming challenge and sensualize yourself performing smoothly, calmly and confidently — in other words by remaining firmly rooted within your O-Zone.

In my early twenties, before I returned to university to study psychology and take my doctorate in the Department of Experimental Psychology at the University of Sussex, I worked as a magazine photojournalist and covered wars and riots around the world. It was partly in response to the suffering, misery, death and destruction I witnessed during those years that I decided to return to university and study psychology in the hope of better understanding both the courage and the depravity I had witnessed and recorded.

One thing I did learn from those experiences is that life is an extremely rare, brief and beautiful gift – all too readily wasted, all too easily destroyed. As with our life so with our talents, skills and abilities all of which, I believe, should always be used to their maximum potential for our own benefit, to enrich the lives of those we love and to further the cause of humanity. To squander those talents through no fault of our own, never to be able to realize our true abilities as a result of barriers lying deep within our subconscious, is an extraordinary tragedy. I believe these procedures of breakthrough breathwork offer one way in which we can eliminate barriers to personal achievement by allowing each one of us, no matter what our current circumstances, to become the people we want to become and were always intended to be.

This concludes my book on breakthrough breathwork. I hope you have found practical and lasting insights from the procedures taught.

Note to Clinical Psychologists and Breathwork Therapists
If you are interested in using any of these procedures in your own professional work with clients and would like further advice or guidance, then please e-mail me at david@dlcltd.com and I will be happy to help.

If you find ways of enhancing or building on the procedures I have described in this book, or use them to treat specific conditions, then I would be equally delighted to hear from you.

Appendix

Graphs showing the electrical patterns in the brain produced by Breathwork Procedures Three–Six.

(1) Brain activity produced by the Relaxing Breath

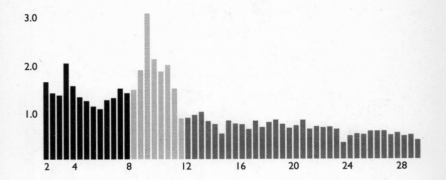

(2) Brain activity produced by the Energising Breath

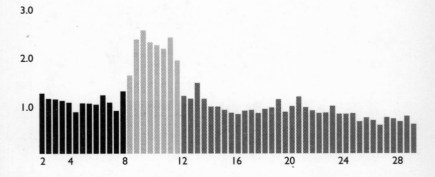

(3) Brain activity produced by the Focused Breath

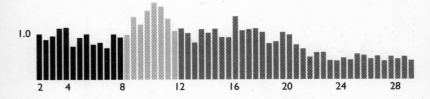

(4) Brain activity produced by the Breakthrough Breathing

References and Bibliography

Acosta, A. and Vila, J. (1990). Emotional Imagery: Effect of Autonomic Response Information on Physiological Arousal. *Cognition and Emotion, 4(2)*, 145–160.

Allen, J. A. (1996). *Perceptual images and the many-to-one principle*. Paper presented at the Toward a Science of Consciousness 'Tucson II', Tucson, Arizona.

Alwyn, S. (1995). *The Controversial New Science of Consciousness. Stairway to the Mind*. New York: Springer-Verlage.

Badawi, K., Wallace, R.K., Orme-Johnson, D. and Rouzere, A.M. (1984). Electrophysiological characteristics of respiratory suspension periods occurring during the practice of the transcendental meditation program. *Psychosomatic Medicine, 46*, 267–276.

Bandura, A. (1986). *Social foundations of thought and action: A social cognitive theory*. Englewood Cliffs, NJ: Prentice Hall.

Banquet, J.P. (1973). Spectral analysis of the EEG in meditation. *Electroencephalography and Clinical Neurophysiology, 35*, 143–151.

Beary, J. F., Benson, H. and Klemchuck, H.P. (1974). A simple psychophysiologic technique which elicits the hypometabolic changes of the relaxation response. *Psychosomatic Medicine. 36*, 115–120.

Beaumont, J.G., Kenealy, P.M. and Rogers, M.J.C. (Eds) (1996). *The Blackwell Dictionary of Neuropsychology*. Cambridge, Mass: Blackwell Publishers.

Benson, H., Dryer, T. and Hartley, L.H. (1978). Decreased CO_2 consumption during exercise with elicitation of the relaxation response. *Journal of Human Stress, 4*, 38–42.

Bird, B.L., Newton, F.A., Sheer, D.E. and Ford, M.A. (1978). Biofeedback training of 40-Nz EEG in humans. *Biofeedback and Self-Regulation. 3(1)*.

Bull, J., Albinson, J.G. and Shambrook, C.J. (1996). *The Mental Game Plan*. Eastbourne, UK: Sports Dynamics.

Butler, R.J., (Ed.) (1997). *Sports Psychology in Performance*. Oxford: Butterworth Heinemann.

Calvin, W.H. (1998). Competing for consciousness: A Darwinian mechanism at an appropriate level of explanation. *Journal of Consciousness Studies, 5(4)*, 389–404.

Cappo, B.M.H. (1984). The utility of prolonged respiratory exhalation for reducing physiological and psychological arousal in non-threatening and threatening situations. *Journal of Psychosomatic Research, 28*, 265–273.

Carroll, D., Marzillier, J.S. and Merian, S. (1982). Psychophysiological changes accompanying different types of arousing and relaxing imagery. *Psychophysiology, 19*, 75–82.

Carter, R. (1998). *Mapping the Mind*. London: Weidenfield and Nicolson.

Chandra, F.A. (1994). Respiratory practices in Yoga. In B.H.L. Timmons, R. (Ed.) *Behavioural and psychological approaches to breathing disorders*. New York: Plenum Press.

Chapell, M.S. (1994). Inner Speech and Respiration: Toward a Possible Mechanism of Stress Reduction. *Perceptual and Motor Skills, 79*, 803–811.

Clark, D.M., Salkovskis, P.M. and Chalkley, A.J. (1985). Respiratory control as a treatment for panic attacks. *Journal of Behaviour Therapy and Experimental Psychiatry, 16(23–30)*.

Clark, M.E. (1990). Effects of paced respiration on anxiety reduction in a clinical population. *Biofeedback and Self-Regulations 15(3)*, 273–284.

Clark, M.F. (1979). The therapeutic applications of physiological control: The effectiveness of respiratory pacing in reducing autonomic, desensitization and subjective distress. *Dissertation Abstracts International, 39*, 4571B–4572B.

Clark, M.F.H. (1980). Effects of paced respiration on affective responses during dental stress. *Journal of Dental Research, 59*, 1533.

Claxton, G. (1997). *Hare Brain Tortoise Mind; Why intelligence increases when you think*. London: Fourth Estate.

Conway, A.V. (1994). Breathing and feeling. In B.H.L Timmons (Ed.) *Behavioural and psychological approaches to breathing disorders*. New York: Plenum Press.

Cotterill, R. (1996). Prediction and Internal Feedback in Conscious Perception. *Journal of Consciousness Studies, 3(3)*, 245–266.

Damas, M.J., Grant, L., Keyon, P., Patel, M.K. and Jenner, F.A. (1976). Respiratory ventilation and carbon dioxide levels in syndromes of depression. *British Journal of Psychiatry, 129*, 457–464.

Damasio, A.R. (1994). *Descarte's Error: Emotion, Reason and the Human Brain*. New York: G.P. Putnam.

Decetty, J., Perani, D., Jeannerod, M., Bettinardi, V., Tadary, B., Woods, R., Mazziotta, J.C. and Fazio, F. (1994). Mapping motor representations with positron emission tomography. *Nature, 371*, 600–602.

Decetty, J., Sjoholm, H., Ryding, E., Stenberg, G. and Ingvar, D.H. (1990). The cerebellum participates in mental activity: tomographic measurements of regional cerebral blood flow. *Brain Research, 535*, 313–317.

Dennett, D.C. (1991). *Consciousness Explained*. London: Allen Lane, The Penguin Press.

DeTroyer A., Estenne. M. (1984). Co-ordination between rib cage muscles and diaphragm during quiet breathing in humans. *Journal of Applied Physiology. 57*: 899–906.

Dimond, S.J. (1980). *Neuropsychology*. London: Butterworths.

Don, N.S. and Moura, G. (1997). Topographic brain mapping of UFO experiences. *Journal of Scientific Exploration, 11(4)*, 435–453.

Eccles, J.C. (1973). The cerebellum as a computer: patterns in time and space. *Journal of Physiology, 229*, 1–32.

Edwards, B. (1981). *Drawing on the Right Side of the Brain*. London: Souvenir Press.

Edwards, S. (1993). *The Heart Rate Monitor Book*. New York: Polar Electro Inc.

Engel, B.T. and Chism, R.A. (1967). Effects of increases and decreases in breathing rate on heart rate and finger pulse volume. *Psychophysiology, 4*, 83–89.

Farhi, D. (1996). *The Breathing Book*. New York: Henry Holt and Co.

Fazey, J. and Hardy, L. (1988). *The inverted-U hypothesis: A catastrophe for sports psychology?* Leeds: The National Coaching Foundation.

Fried, R. (1987). Relaxation with biofeedback-assisted guided imagery: The importance of breathing rate as an index of hypoarousal. *Biofeedback and Self-Regulation, 12(4)*, 273–279.

Gatchel R.J. and Price, K.P. (1979). *Clinical Applications of Biofeedback: Appraisal and Status*. New York: Pergamon Press.

Gellhorn, E. (1937). The influence of oxygen want, hypernea and carbon dioxide excess on psychic processes. *Journal of Psychology, 3*, 161.

Godfrey, S. and Campbell, E.J. (1969). Mechanical and chemical control of breath holding. *Quarterly Journal of Experimental Physiology, 54*, 117–128.

Gora, J. Contrain, I.M. and Trinder, J. (1999). Respiratory-related evoked potentials during the transition from alpha to theta EEG activity in Stage 1 NREM sleep. *Journal of Sleep Research, 8(2)*, 123–134.

Gould, D. and Damarjian, N. (1966). Imagery training for peak performance. In J.L.V.R.B.W. Brewer (Ed.), *Exploring sport and exercise physiology*. Washington DC: American Psychological Association.

Grand, S. (2000). *Creation: Life and How to Make It*. London: The Orion Publishing Group Ltd.

Greiz, E. and Van Den Hout, M.A. (1982). Effects of carbon dioxide-oxygen inhalation on subjective anxiety and some neurovegetative parameters. *Journal of Behaviour Research and Experimental Psychiatry, 13*, 27–32.

Grossman, P. (1983). Respiration, stress, and cardiovascular function. *Psychophysiology, 20(3)*, 284–300.

Haney, J.E. (1976). Skin conductance and heart rate responses to neutral, positive and negative imagery: Implications for covert behaviour therapy procedures. *Behaviour Therapy*, 7, 494–503.

Hanin, Y.L., (Ed.) (2000). *Emotions in Sport*. Champaign, Ill. USA: Human Kinetics.

Harris, V.A., Katkin, E.S. Lick, J.R. and Habberfield, T. (1976). Paced respiration as a technique for the modification of autonomic response to stress. *Psychophysiology, 13,* 386–391.

Hirschman, R., Young, D. and Nelson, C. (Ed.) (1979). *Physiologically based techniques for stress reduction.* Morgantown: West Virginia University Foundation.

Holmes, D.S., McCaul, K.D. and Solomon, S. (1978). Control of respiration as a means of controlling responses to threat. *Journal of Personality and Social Psychology, 36,* 198–204.

Jacob, E. (1989). *Sleep and Dreaming.* London: Faber and Faber.

Kasamatsu, A. and Hirai, T. (1969). An electroencephalographic study of Zen meditation (zazen). *Psychologia, 12,* 205–225.

Kinomura, S., Larsson, J., Gulyas. and Roland, P. (1996). Activation by attention of the human reticulare formation and thalamic intralaminar nuclei. *Science, 271 (512).*

Lambertz, M. and Langhorst, P. (1998). Simultaneous changes of rhythmic organization in brainstem neurons, respiration, cardiovascular system and EEG between 0.05 Hz and 0.5 Hz. *Journal of the Autonomic Nervous Systems, 68,* 58–77.

Lang, P.J. (1979). A bio-informational theory of emotional imagery. *Psychophysiology, 16,* 495–512.

Lang, P.J. et al. (1980). Emotional imagery: Conceptual structure and pattern of somatovisceral response. *Psychophysiology, 17,* 276–306.

Lang, P. J., Bradley, M.M. and Cuthbert, B.N. (1992). A motivational analysis of emotion: Reflex-Cortex Connections. *Psychological Science, 3(1),* 44–49.

Leuner, H. (1984). *Guided Affective Imagery: Mental Imagery in Short-Term Psychotherapy.* New York: Thieme-Stratton.

Levenson, R.W. (1992). Autonomic nervous system differences among emotions. *Psychological Science, 3 (1),* 23–27.

Lewis, D. (1984). *Fight Your Phobia – and Win.* London: Sheldon Press.

Lewis, D. (1986). *The Alpha Plan.* London: Methuen.

Lewis, D. (1992). *Stress for Success.* New York: Carroll and Graf.

Lewis, D (1993). *One Minute Stress Management.* London: Cedar.

Ley, R. (1988). Panic attacks during relaxation and relaxation induced anxiety: A hyperventilation interpretation. *Journal of Behaviour Therapy and Experimental Psychiatry, 19*, 253–259.

Ley, R. (1994). Breathing and psychology of emotion, cognition and behaviour. In B.H.L. Timmons, R. (Ed.) *Behavioural and psychological approaches to breathing disorders*. New York: Plenum.

Libet, B. (1996). Neural Time Factors in Conscious and Unconscious Mental Functioning. In Hamerof, S.R., Kaszniak, A.W. and Scott, A.C. (Eds) *Toward a Science of Consciousness*. Cambridge, Mass: The MIT Press.

Libet, B., Freeman, A. and Sutherland, K. (Eds) (1999). *The Volitional Brain: Towards a neuroscience of free will*. Thorverton: Imprint Academic.

Liggett, D.R.H. (1993). Enhancing the visualisation of gymnasts. *American Journal of Clinical Hypnosis, 35(3)*, 190–197.

Liggett, D. (2000). *Sport Hypnosis*. Champaign II: Human Kinetics.

Liu, Q. (1997). *Chinese Fitness: A Mind/Body Approach*. Boston: YMAA Publications Centre.

Llinas, R.R., U. (1993). Coherent 40-Hz oscillation characterises dream state in humans. *Proceedings of the National Academy of Science, 90 (2078)*.

Longo, D.J.V.S., W. (1984). Respiratory Relief. *Behaviour Modification, 8(3)*, 361–377.

Loring S.H., De Troyer A. Actions of the respiratory muscles. In: Roussos C., Macklem P.T., (Eds.) (1985). *The Thorax*. New York, NY: Marcel Dekker Inc; 327–349. Lung Biology in Health and Disease Series.

Lum, L.C. (1975). Hyperventilation: The tip of the iceberg. *Journal of Psychosomatic Research, 19*, 375–383.

Lum, L.C. (1976). The syndrome of habitual chronic hyperventilation. In O.W. Hill (Ed.) *Modern trends in psychosomatic medicine* (Vol. 3, 196–230). London: Butterworth.

Lum, L.C. (1981). Hyperventilation and anxiety state. *Journal of the Royal Society of Medicine, 74*, 1–4.

Lutz, M. and Liggett, D.R. (1998). *Supercharging visualisation for wild water racing*. (US Canoe and Kayak Team Official Publication): Canoe and Kayak Racing News.

MacLean, P.D. (1992). The Limbic Concept In Trimble, M.R. and Bolwig, T.G. (Eds) *The Temporal Lobes and the Limbic. System* Petersfield: Wrightson Biomedical Publishing Ltd.

Martens, R. (1982). *Imagery in sport*. Paper presented at the Proceedings of the Australian Sports Medicine Federation international conference.

Martens, R. (1982). *Imagery in sport*. In M.L. Howell and A.W. Parker (Eds). Proceedings of the Australian Sports Medicine Federation international conference. Vol. 8. Sports medicine: Medical and scientific aspects of elitism in sport.

Martin, K.A. and Hall, C.R. (1995). Using imagery to enhance intrinsic motivation. *Journal of Sports and Exercise Psychology, 17*, 59–67.

McCaul, K.D., Solomon, S. and Holmes, D.S. (1979). Effects of paced respiration and expectations of physiological and psychological responses to threat. *Journal of Personality and Social Psychology, 37*, 564–571.

McGuigan, F.J. (1970). Covert oral behaviours during the silent performance of language tasks. *Psychological Bulletin, 74(5)*, 309–326.

McKellar, P. (1965). *The investigation of mental images*. Penguin Science Survey (Biological Sciences).

Meduna, L.J. (1947). *Carbon dioxide therapy*. Springfield, II: Thomas.
Miller, G.A., Levin, D.N., Kozak, M.J., Cook, E.W., McLean, A., Lang, P. (1987). Individual differences in imagery and the psychophysiology of emotion. *Cognition and Emotion, 1*, 367–390.

Nixon, P.G.F. and Freeman, L.J. and King, J.C. (1987). Breathing and thinking: Unacknowledged coronary risk factors. *Holistic Medicine, 2*, 133–136.

Nixon, P.G.F., Freeman, L.J. (1988) The 'think test': a further technique to elicit hyperventilation. *Journal of the Royal Society of Medicine* Vol 81.

Norretranders, T. (1991). *The User Illusion: Cutting Consciousness Down to Size*. London: Allen Lane, Penguin Press.

Obrist, P.A., Webb, R.A., Sutterer, J.R. and Howard, J.L. (1970). The cardiac-somatic relationship: Some reformulations. *Psychophysiology, 6,* 569–587.

Obrist, P.A. (1976). The cardiovascular reaction – as it appears today. *Psychophysiology, 13,* 95–107.

Orwin, A. (1971). Respiratory relief: A new and rapid method for treatment of phobic states. *British Journal of Psychiatry, 119,* 635–637.

Pinker, S. (1997). *How the mind works.* Allen Lane, Penguin Press.

Raglin, J.S.T. (1993). Anxiety and performance in track and field athletes: A comparison of the inverted-U hypothesis with the zone of optimal functioning theory. *Personality and Individual Differences, 14,* 163–171.

Rama, S., Ballentine, R. and Hymes, A. (1979). *Science of Breath.* Honesdale, Pennsylvania: Himalayan International Institute of Yoga Science and Philosophy.

Richardson, A. (1967). Mental Practice: A review and discussion. *Research Quarterly, 38,* 95–107, 263–273.

Ryan, E.D. and Simons. J. (1983). What is learned in mental practice of motor skills: A test of the cognitive-motor hypothesis. *Journal of Sports Psychology, 5,* 419–426.

Sheehan, P.W. (1967). A shortened form of Betts' Questionnaire Upon Mental Imagery. *Journal of Clinical Psychology, 23,* 386–389.

Silva, J.M. (1982). Competitive Sport Environments: Performance Enhancement through Cognitive Intervention. *Behaviour Modification, 6(4),* 443–463.

Slater, S.L. and Leavy, A. (1966). The effects of inhaling a 35% CO_2 – 65% O_2 mixture upon anxiety in neurotic patients. *Behaviour Research and Therapy, 4,* 309–316.

Sroufe, L.A. (1971). Effects of depth and rate of breathing on heart rate and heart rate variability. *Psychophysiology, 8,* 648–655.

Strosahl, K.D.A. (1981). Clinical uses of mental imagery: Experimental foundations, theoretical misconceptions, and research issues. *Psychological Bulletin, 89,* (3), 422–438.

Suinn, R.M. (1993). Imagery. In M.M.R. Singer, and L. Tennant (Ed.) *Handbook of research on sport psychology* (492–510). New York: Macmillan.

Surwillo, W.W.H. (1978). Brain electrical activity during prayer. *Psychological Reports, 43(135).*

Swets, J.A.B. (1990). Enhancing Human Performance: An evaluation of 'New Age' Techniques Considered by the U.S. Army. *Psychological Science, 1(2)*, 85–96.

Taylor A. (1960). The contribution of the intercostal muscles to the effort of respiration in man. *Journal of Applied Physiology*, (London). 151: 390–402.

Thyer, B., Papsdorf, J. and Wright, P. (1984). Physiological and psychological effects of acute intentional hyperventilation. *Behaviour Research and Therapy, 22*, 587–590.

B.H.L. Timmons R. (Ed.). (1994). *Behavioural and psychological approaches to breathing disorders.* New York: Plenum.

Trinder, J., Van Beveren, J.A., Smith, P., Kleiman, J. and Kay, A. (1997). Correlation between ventilation and EEG-defined arousal during sleep onset in young adults. *Journal of Applied Physiology, 83(6)*, 2005–2011.

Tucker, B. and Jenkins, S. (1996). The effects of breathing exercises with body positioning on regional lung ventilation. Australian Physiotherapy, Vol 42, No3, 219–227.

Vincent, J-D. (1990). *The Biology of Emotions.* Oxford: Basil Blackwell.

Waitley, D. (1995). *Empires of the Mind.* London: Nicholas Brealey Publishing.

Watson, L. (1984). *Heaven's Breath: A Natural History of the Wind.* London: Coronet.

Watson, L. (1999). *Jacobson's Organ and the remarkable nature of smell.* London: Allen Lane, The Penguin Press.

Watts, F.N.B., A.J. (1987). Lang's Theory of Emotional Imagery. *Cognition and Emotion,* 391–405.

Weinberg, R.S.G. (1999). *Foundations of sport and exercise psychology.* Champaign, IL: Human Kinetics.

Zimmermann, M. (1989). The Nervous System in the Context of Information Theory, in Schmidt, R.F. and Thews, G. (Eds) *Human Physiology* (2nd ed.) Berlin: Springer-Verlag.

Zixin, L., Guo, Li, Y., Zhengyi, S., Zhenyu, Honglin, Z., and Tongling, Z. (1999). *Qigong: Chinese Medicine or Pseudoscience?* Amherst, NY: Prometheus Books.

Index

R

Rama, Swami 64
'readiness potential' 54
rectus abdominis muscles
    139–42
relaxing breath 132–3, 164–77
religious experiencs 49–51
repressed memories 22–3
reptilian brain 46

S

Saver, Jeffrey 50
sensualization 14–15, 20–1,
    27–8, 109–11, 135–6
    for energizing breath 184–6
    for focused breathing 190–2
    identifying a b-lock 195–200
    for relaxing breathing 171–7
    testing 111–14
    training 115–25
Simonides of Ceos 100–1
Simonton, O. Carl 106
Single Photon Emission
    Computed Tomography
    (SPECT) 49
'six pack' 81, 139–42
smell sense 117–18
smoking 73, 162
spine lengthening exercise
    147–8
sport, and visualization 103–4,
    108–9

stress 164–5
supine bicycle exercise 145

T

taste sense 119
telepathy 87–8
Theta waves 90, 91, 93–4
toposcope 88
touch sense 120
transversus abdominis muscle
    142–3

U

unconscious mind 54–8, 200
upside-down breathing 83–4,
    153–4

V

Vincent, Jean-Didier 48
visual sense 115–16
visualization 103–9

W

Walter, Grey 94–5
Watson, Lyall 68
Wittgenstein, Ludwig 59

Z

Zone of Optimal Individual
    Functioning *see* O-Zone